102

Aretin'
Room

A CATHOLIC QUIZ BOOK

THE MACMILLAN COMPANY
NEW YORK · BOSTON · CHICAGO · DALLAS
ATLANTA · SAN FRANCISCO

MACMILLAN AND CO., LIMITED
LONDON · BOMBAY · CALCUTTA · MADRAS
MELBOURNE

THE MACMILLAN COMPANY
OF CANADA, LIMITED
TORONTO

A CATHOLIC QUIZ BOOK

by

Herbert A. Kenny, A.B.

and

Geoffrey P. Keane, A.B., M.D.

1947

THE MACMILLAN COMPANY

NEW YORK

Nihil obstat
Rev. John E. Sexton, D.D.
CENSOR LIBRORUM.

Imprimatur
✠ Richard J. Cushing
ARCHBISHOP of Boston.

July 12, 1945

PRINTED IN THE UNITED STATES OF AMERICA

DEDICATION

This book is lovingly dedicated to our parents.

AUTHORS' PREFACE

THIS BOOK is presented by two Catholic men, a newspaper editor and a doctor, with the prime purpose of providing entertainment.

We recommend that the quizzes be taken in the order in which they appear since some of the answers in later quizzes contain or imply the answers to earlier questions. There are twenty questions in each quiz so that the readers may, if they wish, mark themselves on the basis of five per cent for each question answered correctly. The last two quizzes are of one hundred questions each, and on these the reader may mark himself one per cent for each question answered correctly. These last two quizzes contain questions considered, in general, to be more difficult.

Since the book provides information as well as entertainment, we have taken pains to be accurate. The scope of the material is not encyclopedic, and we have used brief questions and answers wherever possible. Although intended chiefly for Catholics, it should nevertheless be of interest to non-Catholics with a general knowledge of the Church. To Catholics and non-Catholics alike it should provide a ready reference book on a variety of matters.

Much of the material in this book was drawn from standard texts in the respective fields covered by the quizzes. We wish to make special acknowledgment to the following:

The Catholic Dictionary (Editor, Donald Attwater), Macmillan Co., 1942.

The National Catholic Almanac.

The Externals of the Catholic Church, the Rev. John F. Sullivan, D.D., P. J. Kenedy Sons.

We also wish to acknowledge the patience and helpfulness of our families and friends, who have encouraged us by suggestions and enthusiasm. We are grateful to His Excellency, Archbishop Cushing, to various priests of his archdiocese and in particular to the Rev. John E. Sexton, D.D., who read the manuscript for censorship.

HERBERT A. KENNY
GEOFFREY P. KEANE

Feast of St. Richard, 1946
West Roxbury, Massachusetts

FOREWORD

THE COMPILERS of this Catholic "Quiz Book" have put their zeal and erudition to work in a somewhat unusual field, and I am happy to congratulate them and to wish their book every success.

Quiz books have been prepared for almost every department of human interest and information. They have proved stimulants to study, discussion, and entertainment. This book should be no exception; indeed, it should be the more welcome since it directs these to the most fascinating subjects of discussion and speculation.

The proximate purpose of this book is entertainment for Catholics in reviewing their knowledge of the Faith. The ultimate purpose is the increase of that knowledge. Accordingly, study groups, classrooms, and informal meetings of all kinds will greatly benefit from it.

If our people can score well in these quizzes, then they know their Faith. If they find from the use of the book that they do not know it as well as they would wish, then please God these quizzes will prompt them to study it more earnestly.

✠ RICHARD J. CUSHING
Archbishop of Boston

CONTENTS

GOSPELS OF SUNDAYS AND HOLYDAYS
(*Answers on pp. 93–95*)

1. Who said, "Fear not; for behold I bring you good news of great joy . . . for this day is born to you in the city of David a Saviour . . ."?

2. What did Doubting Thomas say when Christ appeared and spoke to him?

3. How many apostles were present at the Transfiguration?

4. When did Christ say, "Begone, Satan . . . The Lord thy God shalt thou worship, and Him only shalt thou serve"?

5. In what parable do these words occur—"Why stand ye here all the day idle"?

6. By whom were these words said—"He is risen: He is not here"?

7. What is the origin of this quotation—"In the beginning was the Word, and the Word was with God, and the Word was God"?

8. Who said, "I am the voice of one crying in the wilderness: Make straight the way of the Lord . . ."?

9. On what occasion did Simon Peter say, "Master, we have toiled all night and taken nothing; but at thy word I will let down the net"?

10. When did Our Lord say, "Did ye not know that I must be about my father's business?"

11. In what connection does the following passage occur, "And another said: I have married a wife and therefore I cannot come"?

12. What was the reply of the centurion when Our Lord offered to go to his house and cure his servant?

13. In what connection does the following passage occur, "And a very great multitude spread their garments in the way; and others cut boughs from the trees and strewed them in the way . . ."?

14. On what occasion did Our Lord say, "Why are ye fearful, O ye of little faith?"

15. What did Christ compare with Solomon in all his glory?

16. In the parable of the Pharisee and the Publican praying in the temple, what was the prayer of the Publican?

17. What was the answer of Our Lord to the question, "And who is my neighbor?"

18. What was Our Lord's reply to the Pharisees who asked Him if it were lawful to give tribute to Caesar?

19. Give the first part of the sentence spoken by Christ which ends with the phrase, ". . . and I know mine and mine know me!"

20. Which is the shortest Gospel text read at Mass during the year?

GROUP TWO

THE PAPACY
(Answers on pp. 95–97)

1. What is the Fisherman's Ring?

2. How is the Pope chosen?

3. What is a Papal Bull?

4. What name has been most frequently chosen by Popes following their election?

5. What is "Peter's pence"?

6. What is an encyclical?

7. What is the tiara?

8. Can you give the titles these men chose when they were elected Pope: Achille Ratti, Eugenio Pacelli, and Giuseppe Sarto?

9. Give three of the nine official titles of the Pope.

10. What Pope originated the present calendar?

11. What is the Rerum Novarum?

12. Who was the first Pope to fly in an airplane?

13. What are the colors of the Papal flag?

14. In what part of the Vatican are the Papal elections held?

15. Give within ten the number of Popes since the founding of the Catholic Church.

16. How many Popes have reigned under the name "Peter"?

17. What is the Holy See?

18. For what is Castel Gandolfo known?

19. St. Peter was the first Pope—who was the second?

20. What is the doctrine of Papal Infallibility?

GROUP THREE

LAY ORGANIZATIONS
(Answers on pp. 97–99)

1. What is the purpose of the Legion of Decency?

2. What is the Sodality of the Blessed Virgin?

3. What is the purpose of the Catholic Order of Foresters?

4. For what well-known Catholic organization do the initials A.O.H. stand?

5. What are the Newman Clubs?

6. What is the Narberth Movement?

7. Who sponsors the Catholic Hour, said to be the world's largest regular religious radio program?

8. With what type of organization do we associate the name Father Theobald Matthew?

9. For what do the initials A.C.T.U. stand?

10. What is the Apostleship of Prayer?

11. What is the purpose of the Society for the Propagation of the Faith?

5

12. What are the objectives of the Holy Name Society?

13. What is the Catholic Youth Organization?

14. What is the Knights of Columbus?

15. What is the Theta Kappa Phi fraternity?

16. What is the National Catholic Welfare Conference?

17. What is the St. Vincent de Paul Society?

18. What is the chief purpose of the Legion of Mary?

19. What is the purpose of the Blackfriars Guild?

20. What is the object of the Catholic Evidence Guild?

GROUP FOUR

THE MASS (1)
(Answers on pp. 99–101)

1. Briefly, what is the Mass?

2. How late in the day may Mass be said?

3. What is the only occasion on which a woman may kneel within the sanctuary of a church during Mass?

4. What is the Missal?

5. Briefly distinguish (a) low Mass, (b) high Mass, (c) solemn high Mass.

6. What does the priest say at the consecration of the bread and wine?

7. Name three of the six vestments the priest wears at Mass.

8. In the liturgical sense, what is an Epistle?

9. At what words does the congregation genuflect during the last Gospel?

10. What is the chalice?

11. What is a purificator?

12. What is the ciborium?

13. What is the paten?

14. What is the ceremony of the Asperges?

15. What is the Canon of the Mass?

16. What part of the Mass is called the Lavabo?

17. What is a Month's Mind Mass?

18. Can you fulfill your Sunday obligation by hearing a Mass on the radio?

19. What are altar cards?

20. Why is the Mass said in Latin?

GROUP FIVE

THE MASS (2)
(Answers on pp. 102–104)

1. Where do we frequently hear the 42nd Psalm, beginning, "Judge me, O God, and distinguish my cause from the nation that is not holy"?

2. In the Mass, what is the Collect?

3. How many Masses may a priest say on Christmas day?

4. On how many days of the year is Mass said?

5. What is the burse?

6. On what two days of the year are gold-colored vestments most frequently worn at Mass?

7. What is the purpose of the three linen (or hemp) altar cloths?

8. Where would you expect to hear the Dies Irae?

9. How many Masses are celebrated in each church on Holy Thursday?

10. What is a field Mass?

11. Distinguish between the Ordinary and the Proper of the Mass.

12. What is the Mass of the Catechumens?

13. What is a Votive Mass?

14. In the absence of a male server, how may a woman assist the priest at Mass?

15. What is a Pontifical Mass?

16. What is a Dialogue Mass?

17. What vestment worn by the priest at Mass is called "the yoke of Christ"?

18. For what intention must the pastor of a parish say Mass on Sundays and holydays of obligation?

19. Except for Masses for the dead, how many times in the year are black vestments worn?

20. At the funeral Mass of a priest, which end of the coffin is nearer the altar?

THE MASS (3)
(Answers on pp. 104–106)

1. What is an acolyte?

2. What is the "Mass of the Faithful"?

3. What is the usual position of the congregation at (1) the Confiteor, (2) the Gospel, (3) the Credo, (4) the Offertory, (5) the Agnus Dei?

4. What is concelebration?

5. What are the common colors of the vestments worn at Mass?

6. What is a catafalque?

7. In reading the Mass with a Missal, tell which of these parts are found in the Ordinary and which in the Proper—(a) the Confiteor, (b) the Gloria, (c) the Epistle, (d) the Gospel, (e) the Creed, (f) the Offering of the bread and wine, (g) the Consecration, (h) the Last Gospel.

8. What are Gregorian Masses?

9. At which part of the altar does the priest stand when he says: (a) the Confiteor, (b) the Introit,

(c) the Gloria, (d) the Pater Noster, (e) the Last Gospel?

10. Where do we frequently hear the following words from Psalm 115, "I will take the chalice of salvation: and I will call upon the name of the Lord"?

11. Where might you see blue vestments at Mass?

12. What have the following Latin phrases in common? —Munda cor meum; Te igitur; Nobis quoque peccatoribus.

13. Are gloves ever worn by the celebrant of a Mass?

14. How many candles must be lighted on the altar at (a) a low Mass said by a priest, (b) a low Mass said by a bishop, (c) a high Mass, (d) a solemn high Mass, (e) a Mass at which the Blessed Sacrament is exposed?

15. Must a priest say Mass every day?

16. Only three Greek words are used in the Mass in the Latin rite. What are they?

17. The celebrant of the Mass receives Holy Communion under the form of both bread and wine, except on one occasion—can you name it?

18. Give within five the number of times the Sign of the Cross is made in the Mass.

19. Place the following parts of the Mass in the order in which they occur: (a) the Lavabo, (b) the Credo, (c) the Preface, (d) the Epistle, (e) the Kyrie Eleison.

20. What is the Red Mass?

GROUP SEVEN

PUBLICATIONS
(*Answers on pp. 106–108*)

1. What religious order publishes the "Catholic World"?

2. Who publishes "The Sign"?

3. Identify "The Commonweal."

4. What type of articles would you find in "The Modern Schoolman" and "The Thomist"?

5. What order publishes "The Queen's Work," "The Messenger of The Sacred Heart," and "America"?

6. Who publishes "Catholic Missions"?

7. What publication printed by the Thomas More bookshop in Chicago is devoted chiefly to reviewing current literature?

12

8. What order publishes "The National Catholic Almanac," and "St. Anthony's Messenger"?

9. What is the name of the magazine published by the Catholic Poetry Society of America?

10. What is the publication of the Newman Club Federation?

11. What is "Our Sunday Visitor"?

12. What group of people would be particularly interested in the "Linacre Quarterly"?

13. With what paper would you associate the names of Dorothy Day and Peter Maurin?

14. What is the "Osservatore Romano"?

15. What order publishes "The Grail," "St. Joseph's Magazine," "Orate Fratres," and "Pax"?

16. What order publishes "The Torch" and "The Holy Name Journal"?

17. What have "The Pilot" and "The Tablet" in common?

18. Who publishes "Field Afar"?

19. What organization publishes the magazine, "Columbia"?

20. Identify "The Register."

GROUP EIGHT

THE BLESSED VIRGIN
(Answers on pp. 108–110)

1. Which month of the year is most popularly associated with the Blessed Virgin?

2. What was the Annunciation?

3. Who was the father of the Blessed Virgin?

4. In which of the Stations of the Cross does the Blessed Virgin meet Christ on His Way to Calvary?

5. What is the Canticle of the Blessed Virgin (the Magnificat)?

6. What does the Church celebrate on December 8?

7. How old was the Blessed Mother at the birth of Christ?

8. What is meant by the purification of the Blessed Virgin?

9. The first miracle performed by Our Lord in His public life was done at the request of His mother —what was the miracle?

10. Distinguish between the Immaculate Conception and the Virgin Birth.

11. To whose care did Christ commend His mother just before He died on the Cross?

12. What is the only event in the life of our Blessed Mother at Nazareth of which the Gospels speak?

13. What is meant by the Assumption of the Virgin Mary?

14. What are the Seven Sorrows of the Blessed Virgin Mother?

15. On what occasion were these words addressed to the Blessed Virgin—"And thy own soul a sword shall pierce"?

16. Who was the mother of the Blessed Virgin?

17. Who addressed to the Blessed Virgin the opening words of the "Hail Mary"?

18. Under which one of her titles is Mary the patron of the United States?

19. On what day is the birthday of the Blessed Virgin Mary celebrated?

20. How old was the Blessed Mother at the time of her Assumption?

SACRAMENTS AND SACRAMENTALS (1)
(Answers on pp. 110–113)

1. What is a sacrament?

2. What are sacramentals?

3. Name the seven sacraments.

4. To confer a sacrament must the one administering it be in the state of grace?

5. Which is the chief sacramental used in the Church?

6. What is Baptism?

7. What is a relic?

8. Define the sacrament of Penance.

9. Can a man validly receive all sacraments?

10. What is the Holy Eucharist?

11. What is a scapular?

12. Define the sacrament of Matrimony.

13. What is ordination?

14. Of how many sacraments may lay persons be the ministers?

15. Which are called the sacraments of the dead?

16. What are banns of marriage?

17. In what words did Our Lord institute the sacrament of the Holy Eucharist?

18. What is Extreme Unction?

19. Of the sacraments, which ones (a) are received only once, (b) may be received more than once, (c) should be received many times by most people?

20. Who may administer the sacrament of Confirmation?

GROUP TEN

SACRAMENTS AND SACRAMENTALS (2)
(Answers on pp. 113–116)

1. What is Holy Water?

2. What is "churching of women"?

3. What is Baptism of desire?

4. What is the seal of confession?

5. Which is the most necessary sacrament?

6. What is the Viaticum?

7. What is a "mixed marriage"?

8. What is general absolution?

9. Suppose a lawyer hears the banns of marriage of one of his clients and through his professional knowledge knows of an impediment to the marriage of the person (such as a previous marriage) —is he bound to reveal his knowledge?

10. What is the punishment for a Catholic who marries before a Protestant minister?

11. Who may confer the sacrament of Holy Orders?

12. What is confession?

13. Can a non-Catholic act as best man or bridesmaid at a Catholic wedding?

14. In the administration of what sacrament does the administrator end by striking or giving a slight blow to the cheek of the recipient and saying, "Peace be with you"?

15. How many times are the banns of marriage published?

16. When Daylight Saving Time is being used, may one take advantage of the extra hour and eat up to one A.M. before receiving communion?

17. What is chrism?

18. In what words did Our Lord institute the sacrament of Baptism?

19. What is the significance of the blessed ashes placed on the foreheads of the faithful on Ash Wednesday?

20. What articles should a household have ready in expectation of a visit from a priest who is going to give communion to some one in the house?

GROUP ELEVEN

SACRAMENTS AND SACRAMENTALS (3)
(Answers on pp. 116–118)

1. Who may receive Holy Communion on Good Friday?

2. Is smoking permitted from midnight until receiving communion, or does it break the fast?

3. Give two other names for the Holy Eucharist.

4. What is transubstantiation?

5. Is a marriage between a Catholic and an unbaptized person valid?

6. Must a saint's name be given in Baptism?

7. In what words did Our Lord institute the sacrament of Penance?

8. What is tonsure?

9. What tribunal of the Church examines and decides upon cases involving validity of marriages?

10. What is Easter water?

11. May a godfather be married to the godchild?

12. Is this statement true or false—"In some instances, Catholics receive Confirmation, as infants, immediately after Baptism"?

13. Is there any rule on wearing gloves while receiving Holy Communion?

14. When does one genuflect on both knees in the church?

15. (a) On what day is the Paschal Candle solemnly lighted, and (b) what does it symbolize?

16. To whom was the devotion of the Miraculous Medal revealed?

17. May all priests administer the sacrament of Penance at any time or place?

18. What is a "reserved case"?

19. What does the priest say in absolution?

20. What is conditional baptism?

GROUP TWELVE

RELIGIOUS ORDERS
(Answers on pp. 118–120)

1. What is the "Benedictine Rule"?

2. What is the adjective used to distinguish members of religious orders from the secular clergy?

3. To whom is the title "Black Pope" applied as a nickname?

4. Which religious order has contributed the greatest number of Popes?

5. Who was Mother Elizabeth Ann Seton?

6. What is the correct name for the Dominican Order?

7. What are the three basic vows which a nun makes on entering a religious order?

8. What is the major distinction between a "sister" and a "nun"?

9. To what religious congregations is the adjective "discalced" applied?

10. Who founded the Society of Jesus?

11. What is the popular title of "The Missionary Society of St. Paul the Apostle in the State of New York"?

12. What are Third Orders?

13. Who founded the Maryknoll Missions, the first American missionary society?

14. Who founded the Paulist Fathers?

15. How long is the term of office of the General of the Jesuits?

16. What well-known religious order was founded by St. Paul of the Cross?

17. What is the principal work of the Christian Brothers?

18. What is the oldest religious order of the Church?

19. What is the best known characteristic of the Trappist order?

20. For what religious orders or congregations do the following abbreviations stand? (a) C.P., (b) C.SS.R., (c) O.F.M., (d) O.M.I.

GROUP THIRTEEN

HISTORY (1)
(*Answers on pp. 120–122*)

1. Who discovered the Mississippi River?

2. Who is called the Father of the American Navy?

3. A great ruler of England, noted for his victories over the Danish invaders, should be equally well known as a lover of learning and religion—can you name him?

4. Who was Charles Carroll of Carrollton (1737–1832)?

5. What Roman Emperor first persecuted the Christians?

6. What was the Renaissance?

7. Who led the Norman Conquest of England?

8. What Belgian cardinal was noted for his heroic patriotism during the first World War?

9. Who was Marco Polo (1251–1324)?

10. Who led the Third Crusade?

11. Who was Vasco da Gama (1469–1524)?

12. What were the Crusades?

13. Who was the first Christian emperor of Rome?

14. Who was Charlemagne (742–814)?

15. For whom is Baltimore named?

16. What were the names of Columbus' three ships?

17. After whom is America named?

18. Who was Ferdinand Foch (1851–1929)?

19. Who discovered the Pacific Ocean?

20. Name one of the two Polish patriots who led American troops during the Revolution.

GROUP FOURTEEN

HISTORY (2)
(Answers on pp. 123–125)

1. What medieval organizations were the forerunners of our labor unions?

2. Who was Clovis (466–511)?

3. For what is Canossa famous?

4. Who were the "Know-nothings"?

5. The great Charles V was Emperor of the Holy Roman Empire and it was of him that it was first said the sun never set on his realm. Of what country was he king?

6. For what is Lepanto famous?

7. Who was the ruler of the Roman Empire at the time of the birth of Christ?

8. Who was called "Le Grand Monarque"?

9. In what British Colony in America was freedom of religion first incorporated into a government charter?

10. Why was Frederick I called "Barbarossa"?

11. What king was called Cœur de Lion?

12. Identify Cardinal Wolsey (1475–1529).

13. What was the nationality of John Cabot?

14. With what country do we associate Henry the Navigator (1394–1460)?

15. What was the significance of the battle of Milvian Bridge?

16. What was the penalty "Ad Bestias"?

17. Who discovered the Philippines?

18. The discoverer of Florida is more noted for his search for the fountain of youth. Who was he?

19. What Spaniards (a) conquered Mexico, (b) conquered Peru?

20. Who were known as the "Prisoners of the Vatican"?

GROUP FIFTEEN

HISTORY (3)
(Answers on pp. 125–127)

1. Who was Jean Louis Lefebvre de Cheverus?

2. Give within one hundred years the date of the First Crusade.

3. What was the Holy Roman Empire?

4. What was the Oxford Movement?

5. What was the Catholic Emancipation Act of 1829?

6. What was the Diet of Worms?

7. Who was Fr. Louis Hennepin (1640–1701)?

8. What Roman emperor moved the capital of the empire from Rome to Byzantium?

9. What is an antipope?

10. For what was the Council of Nicaea of 325 famous?

11. Who was the first native American cardinal?

12. Of what people was Pepin the Short (714–768) the ruler?

13. Who was Don John of Austria (1545–1578)?

14. Who was called "The Uncrowned King of Ireland"?

15. What was the Truce of God?

16. Why was the battle of Tours, A.D. 732, an important world event?

17. Who was Chevalier de Bayard (1475–1524)?

18. Who wrote the Magna Carta?

19. Who discovered the Cape of Good Hope?

20. What office of the French government was held by Cardinal Richelieu (1585–1642), Cardinal Mazarin (1602–1661)?

GROUP SIXTEEN

PRAYERS AND DEVOTIONS (1)
(Answers on pp. 127–130)

1. What is the Confiteor?

2. What is the Rosary?

3. What is Benediction of the Blessed Sacrament?

4. What is meant by the word, "Creed"?

5. What is the devotion of the Nine Fridays?

6. What is a triduum?

7. What is a spiritual bouquet?

8. What is the Stabat Mater?

9. What are the Divine Praises?

10. What is the Apostles' Creed, and why is it so named?

11. Which are the Sorrowful Mysteries of the Rosary?

28

12. Why is the Lord's Prayer so called?

13. What is a Novena?

14. What is the devotion of the Holy Hour?

15. What is the Angelical Salutation?

16. On what day does the solemn veneration of the Cross take place?

17. What is the Tantum Ergo?

18. For what intention are the prayers after Mass offered?

19. What is an aspiration?

20. What is the devotion of the Way of the Cross?

GROUP SEVENTEEN

PRAYERS AND DEVOTIONS (2)
(Answers on pp. 130–133)

1. On what day do we practise the popular custom of visiting seven churches?

2. What is the Miraculous Medal?

3. What is the Divine Office?

4. Can you name the Stations of the Cross?

5. On what days are the Joyful, Sorrowful, and Glorious Mysteries of the Rosary said?

6. How many beads are in the ordinary pocket Rosary?

7. One of the purposes of prayer is to praise God— can you give two other purposes?

8. What is a litany?

9. What is Tenebrae?

10. What is Vespers?

11. What is the Forty Hours' Devotion and what does it commemorate?

12. What is the Memorare?

13. What prayer is called the Angelus?

14. What is a chaplet?

15. What is the Doxology?

16. What indulgence is gained by making the Sign of the Cross?

17. With what religious order is the Rosary particularly associated?

18. The Agnus Dei is a prayer in the Mass and is also the name given to a sacramental. What is that sacramental?

19. What is the "Te Deum"?

20. When is the Nicene Creed recited?

GROUP EIGHTEEN

THE BIBLE
(Answers on pp. 133–135)

1. What is the literal meaning of the word "Bible"?

2. Why is the Douay Version of the Bible so called?

3. What are "apocrypha"?

4. What is a concordance of the Bible?

5. For what are these mountains remembered: (a) Sinai, (b) Ararat, (c) Olivet?

6. What was a Pharisee?

7. The whole New Testament was written in two languages originally. What were they?

8. What is the Apocalypse?

31

9. What is exegesis?

10. Distinguish (a) Judas Machabeus, (b) Jude Thaddeus, (c) Judas Iscariot.

11. What was the Sanhedrin?

12. What is the Vulgate?

13. In the New Testament, what was a Publican?

14. What is a parable?

15. What does the word "Amen" mean?

16. Must Catholics believe that the Old Testament is inspired?

17. Does any indulgence attach to the reading of the Bible?

18. What were "chained Bibles"?

19. What is the Septuagint?

20. What is a canticle?

MUSIC
(Answers on pp. 135–137)

1. Who composed the famous opera, "Pagliacci"?

2. For what is Antonio Stradivari (1650–1737) famous?

3. What great musical invention is generally credited to Guido d'Arezzo (c. 1050), Italian Benedictine monk?

4. Who composed the operas, "William Tell" and "The Barber of Seville"?

5. Who composed the Moonlight Sonata?

6. Who wrote "Oberon" and "Invitation to the Waltz"?

7. Who composed "The Magic Flute"?

8. Who composed "Lucia di Lammermoor" and "Daughter of the Regiment"?

9. What have these adjectives in common—Ambrosian, Gallican, and Mozarabic?

10. What nineteenth-century French composer is famous for his "Faust" and his "Romeo and Juliet"?

11. Who wrote "Over There" and "It's a Grand Old Flag"?

12. Who is often called the father of present-day church music?

13. Who composed the "Blue Danube Waltz"?

14. Who is often called "the inventor of the symphony"?

15. What is the "Motu Proprio"?

16. Who was the most prolific of great operatic composers?

17. Who wrote "The Unfinished Symphony"?

18. What is Gregorian chant?

19. Who wrote the "Second Hungarian Rhapsody"?

20. What very famous Christmas hymn was written by Fr. Josef Mohr (1792–1848) and Franz Gruber (1787–1818)?

THE SAINTS (1)
(Answers on pp. 137–139)

1. What is a saint?

2. Distinguish between (a) beatification and (b) canonization.

3. What is hagiography?

4. What is a patron saint?

5. In commemorating the saints does the Church celebrate their birth or death?

6. Who is the patron saint of carpenters?

7. Identify St. Benedict (d. about A.D. 543).

8. Who was Bernadette Soubirous?

9. Who is the Apostle of Germany?

10. Who is the patron saint of greetings?

11. With what devotional exercise is the name of St. Blaise associated?

12. Who is the patron saint of church music?

13. Who is the most noted patron saint of Ireland?

14. Who is the patron saint of journalists and writers?

15. For what is St. Helen, mother of the Emperor Constantine, famous?

16. Who was the founder of the Order of Friars Minor?

17. Who was the Maid of Orleans?

18. Who was the first martyr?

19. What Irish saint was called the Voyager?

20. Who was St. Isaac Jogues (1607–1646)?

GROUP TWENTY-ONE

THE SAINTS (2)
(Answers on pp. 139–141)

1. Who is the patron saint of England?

2. Who inaugurated the devotion of the crib at Christmas?

3. Who is the patron saint of dentists?

4. What is the most remarkable miracle associated with St. Januarius?

5. Who is the patron saint of automobilists?

6. Who founded the Order of Preachers?

7. Who was the Little Flower of Jesus?

8. Who was called the Angelic Doctor?

9. Who was the first saint of the New World?

10. What saint is called the Apostle of the Negroes?

11. Who was St. Monica (A.D. 333–387)?

12. Who is the patron saint of the Universal Church?

13. What saint was chancellor to King Henry VIII of England?

14. Who founded the Redemptorist Order?

15. Who is patron saint of parish priests?

16. Who was St. Clare?

17. Distinguish between St. Thomas à Kempis and St. Thomas à Becket.

18. What were the native lands of St. Bridget and St. Brigid?

19. Who was St. Vincent de Paul?

20. Who is considered the greatest missionary of the Church since the days of St. Paul?

GROUP TWENTY-TWO

ENGLISH LITERATURE
(Answers on pp. 142–143)

1. What were the miracle plays?

2. Name an American poet killed in World War I whose widow is a poet.

3. Who created the famous fictional detective, Father Brown?

4. For what is Fr. Francis J. Finn, S. J. (1859–1928), well-known?

5. Who wrote "Believe Me If All Those Endearing Young Charms" and "The Last Rose of Summer"?

6. What is the most famous work of the English poet, Geoffrey Chaucer (1340–1400)?

7. Who wrote the words of "A Lost Chord"?

8. Who is famous for his "Apologia Pro Vita Sua"?

9. Who wrote "The Hound of Heaven"?

38

10. What English king is often called "The Father of English Prose"?

11. Who wrote "All for Love" and "The Hind and the Panther"?

12. What is the subject matter of Sir Thomas Malory's (d. 1471) "Morte d'Arthur"?

13. Who wrote "Rebuilding a Lost Faith"?

14. Who was John Lingard (1771–1851)?

15. Who wrote "The Bells of Shandon"?

16. To what religious order did the poets, Gerard Manley Hopkins (1844–1889) and Robert Southwell (1561–1595), belong?

17. Who wrote "The Faith of Our Fathers"?

18. What daughter of a Civil War general was a noted poet and scholar?

19. Who wrote "The Vision of Piers Plowman"?

20. Who is called the Poet of Nuptial Love?

FEASTS AND FASTS
(Answers on pp. 144–146)

1. What is a festival of the Church?

2. What does the Church commemorate on March 25?

3. What is the octave of a feast?

4. Distinguish between fixed and movable feasts.

5. What is Easter Sunday?

6. Are holydays of obligation the same in every country?

7. What is Good Friday?

8. What are the formal names for the following feast days: (1) New Year's, (2) Candlemas Day, (3) Whitsunday?

9. What is the vigil of a feast?

10. On what days has an American Catholic the obligation to attend Mass?

11. What is "Holy Week"?

12. What feast do we celebrate on the first of January?

13. What is Palm Sunday?

14. What does the Church celebrate on November 1?

15. What is Pentecost?

16. Is Ash Wednesday a holyday of obligation?

17. What is Passion Sunday?

18. What event is commemorated in the Mass of the Holy Innocents, December 28?

19. What is Trinity Sunday?

20. What is Old Christmas Day?

GROUP TWENTY-FOUR

DOCTRINE
(Answers on pp. 146–149)

1. What is the science of apologetics?

2. What is theology?

3. What is dogma?

4. Is a Catholic free to believe certain doctrines of the Church while rejecting others?

5. What is a vow?

6. What is meant by (a) the Church Militant, (b) the Church Suffering, and (c) the Church Triumphant?

7. Must Catholics believe that the world was created in six 24-hour days?

8. What is a catechism?

9. What are the principal marks of the true Church?

10. What is meant by Tradition, as used in the Church?

11. What does this passage describe? ". . . there exists in the next life a middle state of temporary punishment, allotted for those who have died in venial sin, or who have not satisfied the justice of God for sins already forgiven."

12. Is the assumption of the Blessed Mother into Heaven an article of faith?

13. What is an indulgence?

14. Does the Catholic Church approve or disapprove of capital punishment?

15. What is revelation?

16. What is meant by saying that a person has reached the age of reason?

17. What is meant by the Incarnation?

18. To gain an indulgence, is it necessary to be in a state of grace?

19. What is the Beatific Vision?

20. Distinguish between contrition and attrition.

GROUP TWENTY-FIVE

SCIENCE
(*Answers on pp. 149–151*)

1. Who discovered wireless telegraphy?

2. For whom is the volt, an electrical unit, named?

3. Who discovered the X-ray?

4. Why is our calendar called the Gregorian calendar?

5. Who was André Marie Ampère (1775–1836)?

6. Who was the inventor of movable type?

7. Who developed the vaccine for the treatment of hydrophobia?

8. Who constructed the first telescope?

9. Who invented the most widely used system of reading for blind persons?

10. For what was Evangelista Torricelli famous?

11. Fr. Julius Nieuwland, C.S.C., who died in 1936, made a very important discovery in the field of chemistry—what was it?

12. For what is René Descartes famous in science?

13. For whom is the galvanometer named?

14. Who was Niclas Koppernigk (1473–1543)?

15. What Augustinian priest made important contributions to the biology of heredity?

16. For what instrument is Pierre Vernier remembered?

17. What teacher of St. Thomas Aquinas is the patron saint of natural sciences?

18. Who wrote "Opus Majus," which has been called "the beginning of modern experimental science"?

19. Who is called the father of modern chemistry?

20. The Jesuit order is particularly bound up with one field of natural science—what is it?

HERESIES AND "ISMS"
(Answers on pp. 151–153)

1. What is heresy?

2. What is polytheism?

3. What does fatalism deny?

4. What is an apostate?

5. Against what religious order did the Jansenists particularly direct their attacks?

6. What was iconoclasm?

7. What was the first great heresy?

8. What is a schism?

9. Distinguish between an infidel and a heathen.

10. What is the name commonly given to the doctrine that God and the universe are identical?

11. What does deism deny?

12. What is agnosticism?

13. Give a simple definition of secularism.

45

14. What was the main doctrine of Calvinism?

15. What two saints distinguished themselves in combating the Albigensian heresy?

16. What two main doctrines did the Pelagians reject?

17. What is the philosophic name of the heretical doctrine that underlay the Manichean and Cathari heresies?

18. What was the distinguishing belief of the Universalist Church?

19. What heretical sect was founded by George Fox?

20. What heresy was indicated by the slogan, "Faith alone [that is, without good works] is sufficient for salvation"?

GROUP TWENTY-SEVEN

OLD TESTAMENT (1)
(Answers on pp. 153–155)

1. What is the Old Testament?

2. What are the opening words of the Old Testament?

3. What is the Pentateuch?

46

4. How many of the Ten Commandments begin with the words "Thou shalt not—"?

5. Was it an apple that Eve ate in the Garden of Eden?

6. Who was born first, Cain or Abel?

7. What wonderful person, other than Solomon, is called the son of David?

8. What was the Deluge?

9. Who built the Ark?

10. Who was commanded by the Lord to sacrifice his son?

11. Who rose from bondage to become governor of Egypt?

12. Who was Moses?

13. What did David use to slay Goliath?

14. For what was Samson noted?

15. What was the Ark of the Covenant?

16. For what was Job in the Old Testament noted?

17. Who was the leader of the Israelites at the fall of Jericho?

18. Name three of the prophetical writers of the Old Testament.

19. How many books are there in the Old Testament?

20. Everyone knows that Genesis is the first book of the Old Testament. What is the last?

GROUP TWENTY-EIGHT

OLD TESTAMENT (2)
(Answers on pp. 155–156)

1. Name the first five books of the Old Testament.

2. What is the meaning of the phrase, "The Ancient of Days"?

3. What city did Cain found?

4. Who were Sem, Cham, and Japheth?

5. What is the tower of Babel?

6. What was the name of Abraham before God changed it?

7. Who was turned to a pillar of salt?

48

8. Who sold his birthright for a bowl of pottage?

9. What was Jacob's ladder?

10. Who worked twice seven years to win his wife?

11. What was the coat of many colors?

12. Name five of the ten plagues of Egypt.

13. Who was Aaron?

14. How long did the Israelites wander in the desert before reaching the promised land?

15. Who was king of Israel before David?

16. For what was Solomon noted?

17. Who was taken up into heaven in a fiery chariot?

18. The first two Books of Kings are sometimes called by what other name?

19. Who were Sidrach, Misach, and Abdenago?

20. In the Book of Genesis, who wrestled with an angel?

FOREIGN LITERATURE
(Answers on pp. 157–158)

1. Who is the national epic hero of Spain?

2. What are the three main divisions of "The Divine Comedy" of Dante Alighieri (1264–1321)?

3. Who was the author of "Don Quixote"?

4. Who was Jean Racine?

5. For what literary work is François René de Chateaubriand (1768–1848) most noted?

6. What was the name of the French beggar-poet about whose life so many novels, plays, light operas, and motion pictures have been made?

7. Who was Molière?

8. Who wrote the "Orlando Furioso"?

9. Who was Giovanni Boccaccio (1313–1375)?

10. What French writer is famous for his fables?

11. What had these two saints in common besides their friendship: St. Teresa of Avila (1515–1582) and St. John of the Cross (1549–1591)?

12. What Italian poet wrote the famous poems, "Jerusalem Delivered" and "Rinaldo"?

13. Who was Jacques Bénigne Bossuet (1627–1704)?

14. Who wrote "The Adventures of Gil Blas"?

15. In what field of literature were the two priests, Lope de Vega Carpio (1562–1635) and Calderón de la Barca (1600–1681), most prolific?

16. Who wrote the historical trilogy, "With Fire and Sword," "The Deluge," "Pan Michael"?

17. Who was Blaise Pascal (1623–1662)?

18. With what literary form is the name of Petrarch (Francesco Petrarca, 1304–1374) associated?

19. In what field of writing was Ludwig von Pastor (1854–1928) famous?

20. Of what country did Luis Vas de Camoëns (1524–1579) write the national epic poem?

PROPHECIES
(Answers on pp. 159–161)

1. In what way was the prophecy of Jacob, foretelling the Messiah, fulfilled—"The sceptre shall not be taken away from Juda . . . till he come that is to be sent . . ." (Gen. 49,10)?

2. Here is an Old Testament prophecy; how was it fulfilled in Christ—"Behold a virgin shall conceive, and bear a son . . ." (Isaias 7,14)?

3. This is an Old Testament prophecy—how was it fulfilled by Christ—"And thou Bethlehem . . . out of thee shall he come forth unto me that is to be the ruler in Israel" (Micheas 5,2)?

4. To what does the following Old Testament prophecy refer—"In that day the root of Jesse . . . him shall the Gentiles beseech" (Isaias 11,10)?

5. What event in the life of Our Lord fulfilled the following Old Testament prophecy—"A voice was heard on high . . . of Rachel weeping for her children . . . because they are not" (Jeremias 31, 15)?

6. What event in the life of Our Lord fulfilled the following Old Testament prophecy—". . . and I called my son out of Egypt" (Osee 11,1)?

7. What event in the life of Our Lord fulfilled the following Old Testament prophecy—"The voice of one crying in the desert: Prepare ye the way of the Lord, make straight in the wilderness the paths of our God" (Isaias 40,3)?

8. What fact in the life of Our Lord fulfilled the following Old Testament prophecy—"I will open my mouth in parables" (Psalm 77)?

9. What events in the life of Our Lord fulfilled the following Old Testament prophecy—"Then shall the eyes of the blind be opened and the ears of the deaf shall be unstopped" (Isaias 35,5)?

10. How is this Old Testament prophecy fulfilled in Christ—"Because he hath done no iniquity, neither was there deceit in his mouth" (Isaias 53,9)?

11. What event in the life of Our Lord fulfilled the following Old Testament prophecy—"Behold thy King will come to thee . . . he is poor, and riding upon an ass, and upon a colt the foal of an ass" (Zacharias 9,9)?

12. What event in the life of Our Lord fulfilled the following Old Testament prophecy—"And they weighed for my wages thirty pieces of silver" (Zacharias 11,12)?

13. What event in the life of Our Lord fulfills the Old Testament prophecy—"I have not turned away

my face from them that rebuked me, and spit upon me" (Isaias 50,6)?

14. What event in the life of Our Lord fulfilled the following Old Testament prophecy—"They parted my garments among them; and upon my vesture they cast lots" (Psalm 21)?

15. How does Our Lord fulfill this Old Testament prophecy—"and he hath borne the sins of many, and hath prayed for the transgressors" (Isaias 53, 12)?

16. By what event in the life of Our Lord was the following Old Testament prophecy fulfilled—". . . and in my thirst they gave me vinegar to drink" (Psalm 68,22)?

17. What does the following prophecy foretell—"But he was wounded for our iniquities, he was bruised for our sins" (Isaias 53,5)?

18. How was this prophecy fulfilled in Christ—". . . the sun and moon are darkened, and the stars have withdrawn their shining" (Joel 2,10)?

19. What event in the life of Our Lord fulfilled the following Old Testament prophecy—"And they shall look upon me whom they have pierced" (Zacharias, 12,10)?

20. What event is prophesied in the following quota-

tion—"Because thou wilt not leave my soul in hell; nor wilt thou give thy holy one to see corruption" (Psalm 15,10)?

GROUP THIRTY-ONE

THE APOSTLES
(Answers on pp. 161–163)

1. Can you name eight of the twelve apostles?

2. Who was Simon Bar Jona?

3. Who is known as the Apostle of the Gentiles?

4. Distinguish between the apostles and the disciples of Our Lord.

5. Which of the evangelists were also apostles?

6. Who was chief among the apostles?

7. What was the Gift of Tongues?

8. How many sets of brothers were there among the twelve apostles?

9. Why do St. Peter and St. Paul have a common feast day?

10. What was the business of St. Matthew before he became an apostle?

11. In what form did the Holy Ghost come upon the apostles?

12. Which of the apostles of Our Lord was called Didymus (the Twin)?

13. In what words did Our Lord establish Peter as the first Pope?

14. Which parts of the New Testament were written by the Beloved Apostle, St. John?

15. What was St. Paul's name before his conversion?

16. Only one of the apostles died a natural death—do you know his name?

17. Name two persons who wrote Epistles in the New Testament.

18. Who was chosen to fill the place of Judas among the apostles?

19. What was St. Peter's trade before he became one of our Lord's apostles?

20. Who was the first apostle called to service by Christ?

ART
(Answers on pp. 163–165)

1. What name is given to pictures in which the Blessed Mother is the central figure?

2. Who painted La Gioconda?

3. Who painted the Sistine Madonna?

4. Who painted the glorious ceiling of the Sistine Chapel?

5. Who painted The Angelus and The Man with the Hoe?

6. In what field did Ghiberti (1378–1455) and Donatello (1386–1466) excel?

7. For what type of painting is Jean B. C. Corot (1796–1875) famous?

8. By what popular name is Tiziano Vecellio (1482–1576) known?

9. What is the "Christ of the Andes"?

10. What is a pietà?

11. For what are the brothers Herbert and Jan Van Eyck famous?

12. What well-known painter and sculptor is also famous for his sonnets?

13. Bartolome Esteban Murillo (1617–1682) was one of the world's greatest painters. What was his favorite subject?

14. What was Michelangelo's last name?

15. To what religious order did Fra Angelico, the painter (1387–1455), belong?

16. Who is generally considered the greatest portrait painter Spain ever produced?

17. Who is known as the Faultless Painter?

18. What noble ruling family of Florence during the Middle Ages were noted for their patronage of the arts?

19. In what city are located the Pitti Palace and the Uffizi with their famous art galleries?

20. What is the Book of Kells?

CHURCH GOVERNMENT (1)
(Answers on pp. 165–167)

1. What is a holyday of obligation?

2. What is a cardinal?

3. Distinguish between annulment and divorce.

4. What is a chaplain?

5. At the death of a cardinal, what is done with his red hat?

6. What is a fast day?

7. What is the liturgy?

8. What is excommunication?

9. Must we abstain from meat on a Friday which falls on a holyday of obligation?

10. What is a bishop?

11. In a papal election, how is the news of a successful ballot first given to the people assembled outside the Vatican?

12. What is Lent?

13. What is the Easter Duty?

14. What is canon law?

15. What is Vatican City?

16. When does Lent end?

17. Does the Church ever allow cremation?

18. What is a day of abstinence?

19. Is a Catholic who deliberately fails to make his Easter Duty automatically excommunicated?

20. What are the principal Holy Seasons of the ecclesiastical year?

GROUP THIRTY-FOUR

CHURCH GOVERNMENT (2)
(*Answers on pp. 168–170*)

1. What is a diocese?

2. How old must a man be to become a priest?

3. What are Ember Days?

4. What is a convent?

5. What is a concordat?

6. What is a dispensation?

7. May a priest practise medicine?

8. Are Catholics permitted to eat frogs' legs on Friday?

9. What is ecclesiastical Latin?

10. How many cardinals are there in the College of Cardinals when it is filled?

11. What is meant by the phrase, "receive the Red Hat"?

12. What is a Eucharistic Congress?

13. In the processes of beatification and canonization, what is the function of the "Devil's Advocate"?

14. What is an imprimatur?

15. What is a parish?

16. What is the reason for Friday abstinence from meat?

17. Must a church necessarily be open some time of the day?

18. How do we reckon the date of Easter?

19. What title is given to the Pope's representative in the United States?

20. May a person who is not a priest become a cardinal?

GROUP THIRTY-FIVE

CHURCH GOVERNMENT (3)
(*Answers on pp. 170–172*)

1. What role does the Postulator-General take in the process of canonization?

2. What is the "ad limina" visit?

3. When did the United States cease to be regarded as a mission country?

4. What is a canonist?

5. Who is the civil ruler of Vatican City?

6. What is a diocesan synod?

7. What is the Cathedraticum?

8. How many years usually elapse between a person's death and the procedure for his beatification?

9. Does a cardinal, by virtue of his rank, have any greater spiritual power than a bishop?

10. What is an œcumenical council?

11. What is the minimum age for advancement to the rank of bishop?

12. What is a celebret?

13. What is a diocesan chancery?

14. Are you required to make your Easter duty in your own parish?

15. What is the distinction between an auxiliary bishop and a coadjutor bishop?

16. What is meant by the election of a cardinal "in petto" (or "in pectore")?

17. What is an interdict?

18. What is the meaning of the word "laity"?

19. What is the Vatican "Yellow Book"?

20. What is a consistory?

ARCHITECTURE
(Answers on pp. 173–174)

1. What is a baptistery?

2. The cathedrals of St. Etienne at Caen and the cathedral and famous leaning bell tower at Pisa are what type of architecture?

3. What is the most characteristic feature of Gothic architecture?

4. Is the floor plan of St. Peter's Cathedral in Rome in the form of a Latin cross or a Greek cross?

5. What type of architecture is St. Patrick's Cathedral in New York?

6. What is a campanile?

7. What is a flying buttress?

8. What designer of the famous campanile at Florence is also known as the Father of Modern Painting?

9. For what is the town of Carrara in Italy noted?

10. What is a gargoyle?

11. What French cathedral is world-famous for the

blue of its stained glass windows, depicting scenes in the life of the Blessed Mother?

12. What type of architecture is St. Peter's in Rome?

13. What architect planned the city of Washington, D. C.?

14. The cathedral of Notre Dame at Paris and the famous cathedrals at Rheims and Chartres are what type of architecture?

15. What is the largest Catholic church in England?

16. The famous Cathedral of St. Mark in Venice and Westminster Cathedral in England are what type of architecture?

17. Did Gothic architecture find more favor in the northern or southern countries?

18. By whom was the White House at Washington designed?

19. How many people can be assembled in St. Peter's, at Rome?

20. How did Gothic architecture get its name?

SYMBOLISM
(Answers on pp. 174–176)

1. What symbol, used by the Church, is best known?

2. For whom is the Dove a symbol?

3 For whom is the Lamb a symbol?

4. What is the symbolic significance of ears of wheat coupled with bunches of grapes?

5. What is an aureole?

6. Of what is the lily the symbol?

7. Whom and what does a dragon or a serpent symbolize?

8. In church symbolism, what does an anchor stand for?

9. What does a ship symbolize in church usage?

10. For what do the initials I H S stand?

11. What plant symbolizes martyrdom?

12. What·is a St. Andrew's Cross?

13. Why do Catholic churches usually have three doors?

14. Of whom is a fish the symbol?

15. For what does A. M. stand when used in designs in churches?

16. What is a chirho?

17. Why is the pelican an emblem of Christ in the Blessed Sacrament?

18. For what do the Greek letters A (Alpha) and Ω (Omega) stand?

19. Why is a bishop's crozier hooked at the top and pointed at the bottom?

20. Give the symbols of three of the four Evangelists.

GROUP THIRTY-EIGHT

NEW TESTAMENT (1)
(Answers on pp. 176–178)

1. To what is the name "The Holy Rood" applied?

2. Without reciting them, state what are the eight Beatitudes.

3. When was Christ born?

4. What was the Last Supper?

5. What were the names of the three Magi?

6. What was the flight into Egypt?

7. What was the trade of St. Joseph?

8. Why was Christ called the Galilean?

9. What was the pagan Pontius Pilate's title?

10. Was Our Lord baptized, and if so, by whom?

11. What was the duration of Christ's public life?

12. What preceded the temptation of Our Lord by Satan?

13. On what occasion were these words spoken, "Ye men of Galilee, why stand you looking up to heaven"?

14. What remarkable event took place immediately after the baptism of Our Lord?

15. What language did Christ speak while on earth?

16. What does the word "Messias" mean?

17. How many days passed between the Ascension of Our Lord and the descent of the Holy Ghost upon the apostles?

18. Do the Gospels mention any instance of Christ writing?

19. Among the miracles which Our Lord performed, three persons were raised from the dead—can you identify them?

20. What is the last line of the New Testament?

GROUP THIRTY-NINE

NEW TESTAMENT (2)
(Answers on pp. 178–180)

1. Who, besides Our Lord, were crucified on Calvary?

2. Who was responsible for bestowing the name Jesus on Our Lord?

3. What is "The Acts of the Apostles"?

4. Who were the parents of St. John the Baptist?

5. Which are the historical books of the New Testament?

6. To whom is the title, "The Father of Lies," given?

7. Who are the Evangelists?

8. Who was the first apostle called to the apostolate by Our Lord?

9. How were both St. John the Baptist and St. Paul killed?

10. Of whom did Christ say that she "hath chosen the best part"?

11. What was the answer to the Pharisees who questioned Christ on the punishment of the woman taken in adultery?

12. Why is the name of Ananias synonymous with a liar?

13. What was the Cenacle?

14. Why was St. Peter crucified upside down?

15. Of whom was Our Lord speaking, when He asked, "What went you into the desert to see?"

16. In what connection does the sentence—"And Jesus wept"—occur in the New Testament?

17. Which one of the four Evangelists was a physician?

18. What is the origin of the frequently quoted question—"Oh death, where is thy sting?"

19. Distinguish between Lazarus of the parable and Lazarus of the miracle.

20. What action of the apostles is emulated in making a novena?

GROUP FORTY

THE PASSION OF OUR LORD
(Answers on pp. 181–183)

1. What is the Passion of Our Lord?

2. For what is the Garden of Gethsemane famous?

3. Who accompanied Our Lord to the Garden of Gethsemane on the night of His Agony?

4. What is the significance of this passage—"And forthwith he came to Jesus, and said: Hail, Rabbi: and he kissed Him . . ."?

5. What price was Judas promised for betraying Our Lord?

6. Who used the phrase, "Ecce Homo" (Behold the Man)?

7. Who were Annas and Caiphas?

8. In what connection does the following sentence occur—"And the cock crowed"?

9. How did Judas Iscariot die?

10. What is Calvary?

11. To whom did Christ say, "Weep not for Me, but weep for yourselves and for your children"?

12. Why do we remember St. Veronica?

13. Who was made to help Jesus carry His cross on the way to Calvary?

14. Three Marys were with Our Lord on Calvary—can you name them?

15. For what do the initials I.N.R.I. stand?

16. What part did Barabbas play in the Passion of Our Lord?

17. Who said, at the foot of the Cross, "Indeed, this was the Son of God"?

18. What were the Seven Last Words of Christ?

19. In whose tomb was Christ's body buried?

20. What is the Redemption?

SPECIAL GROUP ONE

(Answers on pp. 183–193)

1. What is the Decalogue?

2. Name the three angels mentioned by name in the Holy Scriptures.

3. What name is given to the ceremonial headgear worn by bishops?

4. Was St. Francis of Assisi (1181–1226) a priest?

5. Name three of the historical books of the Old Testament.

6. In the ordination of a priest the phrase occurs, "Thou art a priest forever according to the order of Melchisedech." Who was Melchisedech and why is he significant?

7. Distinguish Levite and Leviticus.

8. What is the Laetare Medal?

9. What was the site of the first international Eucharistic Congress held in the United States?

10. Name three of the seven corporal works of mercy.

11. Which of these three cathedrals is located on an

island: (a) Notre Dame of Paris, (b) Cologne, (c) Milan?

12. What is the breviary?

13. In international understanding, what is the rank of a cardinal?

14. Who was Catherine Tekakwitha (1656–1680)?

15. Name the four cardinal virtues.

16. Who is Paul Yu-Pin?

17. Who was John Boyle O'Reilly (1844–1890)?

18. Where do these words occur—"Rejoice with me, because I have found my sheep which was lost"?

19. What is the Paraclete?

20. Who besides Elias, in the Old Testament, was taken out of the world without being subject to death?

21. What part of the human body takes its name from Bartolomeo Eustachius (1500–1574)?

22. During the reign of what Roman emperor did St. Peter suffer martyrdom?

23. What is the biretta?

24. What is a catechumen?

25. What activity is common to Correggio, Bellini, Tintoretto?

26. With what historical event was Louis Joseph Montcalm (1712–1759) associated?

27. In what country did the artists, El Greco (1545–1614), Murillo (1617–1680), and Goya (1746–1824) do their work?

28. Who was Manuel L. Quezon?

29. What are the three conditions required for mortal sin?

30. With what field of science is the name of Giovanni Morgagni (1682–1771) associated?

31. For what is Alban Butler (died 1773) famous?

32. What was the name of Pope Pius XII, before his elevation to the Papacy?

33. What is the name of the vessel in which the Blessed Sacrament is exposed at Benediction?

34. Give three of the six precepts of the Church.

35. What is the pyx?

36. Of whom is it said, "for theirs is the kingdom of Heaven"?

37. Which are the Glorious Mysteries of the Rosary?

38. What is the "Index"?

39. What are rubrics?

40. What is a cowl?

41. Who sculptured the marble David at Florence?

42. Name a recent president of Notre Dame University who was a well-known poet (author of "Cloister and Other Poems," "A Rime of the Road and Other Poems").

43. Locate (a) the transepts or (b) the nave of a church.

44. Must sponsors at Baptism be Catholics?

45. What does the phrase "Nihil Obstat" mean?

46. What is a crozier?

47. In the Arthurian legends, what was the Holy Grail?

48. What is the oldest Catholic college in the United States?

49. What is Low Sunday?

50. Of whom is it said, "for they shall be called the children of God"?

51. What have the following men in common—(a) Charles J. Bonaparte, (b) James A. Farley, (c) Frank C. Walker?

52. Which of the Ten Commandments is violated by blasphemy?

53. Who discovered Canada?

54. Who was Father Damien de Veuster (1840–1889)?

55. Where do these words occur—"For though I should walk in the midst of the shadow of death, I will fear no evils, for thou art with me. Thy rod and thy staff, they have comforted me"?

56. What are catacombs?

57. "The Collegians" has been called the "best of all Irish novels." Who wrote it?

58. Who was called the Prince of Paradox?

59. Who wrote, "Maryland, My Maryland"?

60. Who wrote, "Come Rack, Come Rope" and "Oddsfish"?

61. What part of a church is the sanctuary?

62. "The Keys of the Kingdom," by A. J. Cronin, was a best seller. Can you identify the source of the title?

63. Who may be ordained a priest?

64. What do the initials R.I.P. stand for?

65. What is the literal meaning of the word, "Gospel"?

66. What is Maundy Thursday?

67. In conversation, how would you address—(1) the Pope, (2) a Cardinal, (3) a Bishop?

68. Who were described by Our Lord as "the salt of the earth"?

69. What is a sacristy?

70. For what is the town of Oberammergau famous?

71. Was Cardinal Newman a bishop?

72. For what should the Vatican Council of 1869–1870 be remembered?

73. According to the Old Testament what "is the beginning of wisdom"?

74. For what do the initials S.T.D. after a priest's name stand?

75. With what college is the name of the great football coach Knute Rockne associated?

76. Give the opposite virtue for the following deadly sins—(1) pride, (2) lust, (3) envy, (4) gluttony.

77. For what is Pedro Alvarez Cabral (1460–1526) famous?

78. To what saint do we customarily pray when we wish to find a lost article?

79. What does "Confiteor" mean?

80. With the annexation of the Papal States in 1870, the Pope lost the territory over which he was the temporal ruler. When was his temporal sovereignty restored?

81. What is the name of the large, embroidered cloak worn by the priest at Benediction?

82. Who was the original "Boston Strong Boy"?

83. What is the literal meaning of the name Christ?

84. How many liturgical languages flourish in the Church?

85. On which side of the altar is the pulpit usually placed?

86. What procedure is followed by a lay person in administering Baptism?

87. What is the literal meaning of the word, "Christmas"?

88. Finish the following verse from Psalm 69—"O God, come to my assistance . . ."?

89. What is the literal meaning of the word, "Advent"?

90. Of whom is it said, ". . . for they shall see God"?

91. Give another name for the Sea of Galilee.

92. To whom is the title, "The Fisherman," given?

93. Which of the four Evangelists did not write his gospel in Greek?

94. What does the priest say as he places the Holy Eucharist in the mouth of each person at Holy Communion?

95. From what source does the Church get the ashes used on Ash Wednesday?

96. Name the five liturgical colors.

97. What is the Ecclesiastical Year?

98. Who was the Venerable Bede (673–735)?

99. Who was Pietro Yon (1886–1944)?

100. What are the Stigmata?

SPECIAL GROUP TWO

(Answers on pp. 194–204)

1. When is the "Regina Coeli" recited?

2. What was the Donation of Pepin?

3. The Council of Trent lasted from 1545 to 1563— can you tell for what it is notable?

4. What is a dalmatic?

5. Who was the central character of the play "Second Spring"?

6. Who said—"God loveth a cheerful giver"?

7. In what connection does the name Malchus occur in the New Testament?

8. What is the full official title of the Holy Name Society?

9. With what state is the memory of Junipero Serro attached?

10. In what field were these three men distinguished, James Mangan (1803–1849), Aubrey de Vere (1814–1902), Lionel Johnson (1867–1902)?

11. Complete the following quotation—"The heavens shew forth the glory of God—"

12. Name the Popes who (a) anathematized Martin Luther, (b) refused to sanction the divorce of Henry VIII of England from Catherine of Aragon?

13. The conversions of what men are recounted in (a) "En Route," (b) "The Long Road Home," (c) "Now I See," (d) "Apologia Pro Vita Sua," and (e) "The Emancipation of a Free Thinker"?

14. What were the May Laws of 1873?

15. On what occasion did the high priests and the Pharisees resolve on the death of Jesus?

16. Complete the following quotation—"The fool hath said in his heart . . ."

17. To what religious order did St. Bernard of Clairvaux belong?

18. The members of what religious order were called "The Hounds of God"?

19. Give within two the number of various scapulars approved by the Church.

20. What is meant by becoming a god-parent "by proxy"?

21. Who was John Sobieski?

22. What Doctor of the Church bears the title, "Father of Orthodoxy"?

23. What is the stone in a cardinal's ring?

24. What is the literal meaning of the word, "Lent"?

25. Name three of the seven spiritual works of mercy.

26. Who wrote the "Canticle to the Sun"?

27. While placing ashes on the forehead of the faithful on Ash Wednesday, what does the priest say?

28. What is bination?

29. With what country is Bernardo O'Higgins associated?

30. Who was the first English printer?

31. Who is known as "The Glacier Priest"?

32. The following is a quotation from the 25th Psalm. Where is it frequently heard? "I will wash my hands among the innocent."

33. What is the "ratio studiorum"?

34. Is it permissible for a woman to sing in a sanctuary choir?

35. What is compline?

36. To what church dignitary is the title "Your Beatitude" applied?

37. Who was Richard Crashaw?

38. What is St. Malachy's prophecy?

39. For what does the term, "feria," stand?

40. Who is known as "the poet priest of the South"?

41. Who was the founder and first director of the Paulist Choristers?

42. What had the authors of the novels "Fabiola" and "Callistus" in common?

43. What religious order was founded by (a) St. Francis de Sales, (b) St. Angela of Brescia, (c) St. Alphonsus Liguori, (d) St. Clare of Assisi?

44. To what does the name, Paralipomenon, refer?

45. How long did the waters cover the earth after the rainfall of the Deluge?

46. Domenico Theotocopuli is one of the world's most famous artists. By what nickname is he commonly known?

47. What is a Black Madonna?

48. Who was Richard Challoner?

49. What does the bishop say when he anoints the recipient of confirmation?

50. Who are called the Doctors of the Church?

51. What is the literal meaning of Pentecost?

52. What are the gifts of the Holy Ghost?

53. What famous Italian painter of the sixteenth century was nicknamed "Il Furioso"?

54. Who wrote the line, "Abandon hope all ye who enter here . . ."?

55. What is the only day of the year on which the Church prays publicly and solemnly for those outside her fold?

56. What is meant by the phrase, "anathema sit"?

57. Why is the number of cardinals fixed at seventy?

58. Name two monastic groups who wear sandals.

59. What is the literal meaning of the word "Calvary"?

60. Who was Peter Paul Rubens?

61. Who was "good King Wenceslaus," celebrated in the popular Christmas carol?

62. Identify Martin de Porres (1579–1639)?

63. What is Shrove Tuesday?

64. What is the Tyburn Walk?

65. What is the most famous shrine in (a) Mexico, (b) Canada, (c) France?

66. What are Rogation Days?

67. What unique distinction has the late Fr. Charles Constantine Pise (1801–1866)?

68. How many Catholics were members of the first Constitutional Convention?

69. How many days are prescribed for the burial ceremonies on the death of a Pope?

70. For what spiritual literary work is St. Ignatius Loyola noted?

71. For what was Jacopone da Todi (1228–1306) famous?

72. What percentage of the College of Cardinals must one get to be elected Pope?

73. Give within ten years the year of canonization of St. Joan of Arc (1412–1431).

74. Of the eight decorations awarded by the Pope, which one may be given to non-Catholics?

75. What is the "Ave bell"?

76. How many candles are used in the service Tenebrae?

77. What is the highest decoration a Pope can give a layman?

78. Distinguish between a residential bishop and a titular bishop.

79. Does the Sistine choir sing with or without accompaniment?

80. Two Catholics have been Chief Justices of the United States Supreme Court. What were their names?

81. When was the doctrine of the Immaculate Conception promulgated?

82. Must one be a Swiss citizen to be in the Swiss Guard?

83. What name is given to the first council of the Church?

84. What is an achiropoeta?

85. What is the most noted work of the historian John D. G. Shea (1824–1892)?

86. Name one of the two guards, other than the Swiss Guard, in the Vatican.

87. What is an aliturgical day?

88. Who presides over a Plenary Council of the United States?

89. For what do the initials A. M. D. G. stand?

90. What is meant by the term "Uniate" when applied to a church?

91. Before a person may be beatified or canonized, a certain number of miracles through his intercession must be shown—do you know how many?

92. On what occasions are the following recited—

(a) the Athanasian Creed, (b) the Creed of the Council of Trent?

93. Who wrote the hymns sung at Benediction—"O Salutaris" and "Tantum Ergo"?

94. Who was Nicholas Brakespeare?

95. In the Mass, what is the "kiss of peace"?

96. What is the Ordo?

97. How is a bishop addressed in England and Canada?

98. Who was the first of the twelve apostles to die for Christ?

99. Who founded the city of Quebec?

100. What are the four last things to be remembered?

ANSWERS

GOSPELS OF SUNDAYS AND HOLYDAYS

1. The angel who announced the birth of Christ the Lord to the shepherds near Bethlehem (Midnight Mass of Christmas Day).

2. "My Lord and my God" (Low Sunday).

3. Three—Peter, James and John (2nd Sunday in Lent).

4. After the third temptation by Satan in the desert (1st Sunday in Lent).

5. In the parable of the householder who hired laborers for his vineyard, paying those he hired first the same as those hired last—"So shall the last be first, and the first last" (Septuagesima Sunday).

6. These words, announcing the Resurrection, were said to Mary Magdalen and Mary, the mother of James, by the angel at the sepulchre of Our Lord (Easter Sunday).

7. This is the beginning of the Gospel of St. John, and is read as the Last Gospel in most Sunday Masses.

8. St. John the Baptist, when asked if he were the Christ (3rd and 4th Sundays of Advent).

9. On the occasion of the miraculous draught of fishes in the lake of Genesareth. After the miracle, Our Lord said to Simon, "Fear not; for henceforth thou shalt catch men" (4th Sunday after Lent).

10. In reply to His mother who had reproached Him for staying behind in the temple at Jerusalem, where she and St. Joseph had found Him sitting among the doctors (Sunday in Octave of Epiphany).

11. It occurs in the parable of the man who made a supper, and the invited guests make excuses not to come—"I have bought a farm, I have bought a yoke of oxen" (2nd Sunday after Pentecost).

12. "Lord, I am not worthy that thou shouldst enter under my roof: But only say the word, and my servant shall be healed" (3rd Sunday after Epiphany; 24th Sunday after Pentecost).

13. This is from the Gospel of St. Matthew, as read on Palm Sunday at the blessing of the palms, and describes the triumphal entry of Jesus into Jerusalem.

14. When the disciples wakened him during the storm at sea, saying, "Lord, save us, we perish" (4th Sunday after Epiphany; 24th or 25th Sunday after Pentecost).

15. The lilies of the field (14th Sunday after Pentecost).

16. He struck his breast, saying: "O God, be merciful to me a sinner" (10th Sunday after Pentecost).

17. The parable of the Good Samaritan, which Jesus supplemented with the admonition, "Go, and do thou in like manner" (12th Sunday after Pentecost).

18. "Then saith he to them: Render therefore to Caesar the things that are Caesar's and to God the things that are God's" (22nd Sunday after Pentecost).

19. "I am the Good Shepherd" (2nd Sunday after Easter).

20. The Gospel as read on New Year's Day, the Feast of the Circumcision, less than thirty-five words. This text is also read on the Feast of the Holy Name.

GROUP TWO ANSWERS

THE PAPACY

1. A signet ring worn by the Pope, engraved with the effigy of St. Peter fishing from a boat, and encircled with the name of the reigning Pope.

2. By election by members of the College of Cardinals. A two-thirds majority is required.

95

3. It is a papal document sealed with leaden seals used chiefly in appointing bishops.

4. John. It has been selected twenty-three times.

5. A voluntary contribution raised among Catholics for maintenance of the Pope.

6. It is a circular letter issued by the Pope to the bishops treating matters concerning the general welfare of the Church.

7. The papal crown with three diadems.

8. Pius XI, Pius XII, and Pius X.

9. His Holiness the Pope: Bishop of Rome and Vicar of Jesus Christ: Successor of St. Peter: Prince of the Apostles: Supreme Pontiff of the Universal Church: Patriarch of the West: Primate of Italy: Archbishop and Metropolitan of the Roman Province: Sovereign of the State of Vatican City.

10. Pope Gregory XIII in 1582.

11. The title given to the encyclical issued May 15, 1891, by Pope Leo XIII on the condition of labor. It refutes the false theories of the Socialists and defends the right of private ownership.

12. Pope Pius XII while he was still cardinal.

13. Yellow and white; charged with crossed keys and the triple tiara.

14. In the Sistine Chapel.

15. 263.

16. Only one—St. Peter, the Apostle, the first Pope.

17. The term "Holy See" designates Rome, the official seat of the Pope, and also designates the power of the Pope personally.

18. It is the Pope's summer home.

19. St. Linus.

20. This doctrine teaches that the head of the Church is preserved by divine assistance from teaching error in matters of faith and morals.

GROUP THREE ANSWERS

LAY ORGANIZATIONS

1. To prevent the showing of obscene and lascivious motion pictures.

2. It is an association in honor of the Blessed Virgin, founded in 1574 by the Jesuits.

3. It is a fraternal insurance society with a religious, social, and charitable program.

4. Ancient Order of Hibernians.

5. They are organizations of Catholic students in secular universities, for the purpose of protecting their Christian faith.

6. A movement begun in Narberth, Pa., in 1929, to explain Catholic matters to non-Catholics by means of friendly letters and pamphlets by lay Catholics.

7. The National Council of Catholic Men in collaboration with the National Broadcasting Company.

8. Total abstinence societies.

9. Association of Catholic Trade Unionists, progressive labor organization, founded by a New York priest and carried on by Catholic unionists.

10. It is a pious association engaged in promoting the interests of the Heart of Jesus by offering Him prayers and good works.

11. To assist the missions by prayers and alms.

12. To encourage frequent communion and to discourage profanity and blasphemy.

13. A federation, nation-wide, of boys' clubs under

diocesan direction to guide the cultural and athletic activities and care for their spiritual welfare.

14. A Catholic fraternal organization for men founded in 1882 by the Rev. Michael J. McGivney at New Haven, Conn.

15. A Greek letter fraternity for Catholic men at non-Catholic universities.

16. A common agency organized in 1919 under the bishops of America to promote the welfare of the Catholics in the United States.

17. An organization founded in 1833 by Frederic Ozanam to provide aid for the poor.

18. To restore lapsed and negligent Catholics to the practice of their religion.

19. To sponsor and coördinate Catholic dramatic groups.

20. The diffusion of Catholic truth by means of out-door speaking.

GROUP FOUR ANSWERS

THE MASS (1)

1. It is the unbloody renewal of the Sacrifice of Our Lord upon the Cross.

2. According to the present law of the Church, Mass may be begun as late as one o'clock in the afternoon. In wartime, later Mass is permitted for the Armed Forces.

3. During a nuptial Mass.

4. The Missal is the Mass Book containing all the prayers said by the priest during the Holy Sacrifice.

5. (a) In low Mass, the priest reads or recites all the prayers, (b) In high Mass, the priest sings the Mass, (c) In solemn high Mass, the celebrant is assisted by a deacon and subdeacon.

6. At the consecration of the bread, "For this is My body." At the consecration of the wine, "For this is the chalice of My blood of the new and eternal testament: the mystery of faith; which for you and for many shall be shed unto the remission of sins."

7. Amice, alb, cincture, maniple, stole, chasuble.

8. It is a selection read at Mass after the Collects and is often taken from one of the letters, or Epistles, of the Apostles.

9. "Et Verbum caro factum est et habitavit in nobis." (And the Word was made flesh and dwelt among us.)

10. The cup in which the wine is consecrated in the Mass.

11. A piece of white linen used for cleaning the chalice and wiping the lips and fingers of the celebrant of a Mass.

12. The vessel in which the Sacred Hosts are kept for distribution at Communion.

13. The plate on which the priest puts the Host which he offers and consecrates in the Mass.

14. It is the sprinkling of holy water over the people at a high Mass.

15. It is that part of the Mass from the end of the Sanctus to the beginning of the Pater Noster. It contains the Consecration, and is called the Canon (rule or standard) because it is practically unchangeable in every Mass.

16. The point in the Mass when the priest washes his hands.

17. A Mass of remembrance for the dead, said thirty days after the death of the deceased.

18. No. One must be physically present.

19. Cards printed with certain invariable sections of the Mass and left standing on the altar for the convenience of the priest.

20. It is the official language of the Church and, not

being in popular use, is not subject to change of meaning.

GROUP FIVE ANSWERS

THE MASS (2)

1. These verses are said by the priest at the foot of the altar, beginning Mass.

2. It is a short variable prayer, changeable with the feast or season, commonly recited before the Epistle.

3. Three, in honor of the threefold birth of our Saviour —His eternal birth in the bosom of His father; His temporal birth in Bethlehem; His spiritual birth in the hearts of the just.

4. On every day except Good Friday. Since the celebration on Good Friday is performed with a previously consecrated Host, it is not really the Mass.

5. The burse is a square bag or container, resembling a flat pocketbook, designed to hold the corporal when it is carried to and from the altar.

6. On Easter Sunday and Christmas.

7. They are used out of reverence to the Precious Blood, which would be absorbed by the cloths, if

it were accidentally spilled. They also have a symbolic significance.

8. It is a hymn usually sung at requiem Masses.

9. One, during which two Hosts are consecrated—one for use on Good Friday in the Mass of the Presanctified.

10. A Mass that is celebrated in the open; in time of war, or on special occasions with the bishop's permission.

11. In the Ordinary are contained the prayers said at most Masses, while in the Proper are contained those prayers suitable for the particular day or occasion.

12. It is that part of the Mass up to and including the Credo. In early times, those who were taking instruction in the faith (the catechumens) were permitted to assist at Mass only to this point.

13. It is Mass offered for a special intention not corresponding to the office of the day on which it is celebrated.

14. By making the responses from beyond the communion rail—the priest serves himself at the altar under these conditions.

15. A high Mass celebrated by a bishop.

16. A low Mass at which the responses ordinarily spoken by the server are given aloud by the congregation.

17. The chasuble.

18. For the members of his parish—the Mass which he says for this intention is known as the Missa pro populo.

19. Once, on Good Friday.

20. The priest's head is nearer to the altar to signify that it was his role to speak to the faithful in life and to instruct them.

GROUP SIX ANSWERS

THE MASS (3)

1. An acolyte is one who aids, in a subordinate way, those who officiate at various sacred rites—an altar boy is an acolyte.

2. This name is given to the Mass from the Offertory to the Conclusion because in the early centuries of the Church only those who were baptized were allowed to be present after the Credo.

3. (1) Kneeling, (2) Standing, (3) Standing, (4) Sitting, (5) Kneeling.

4. It is the rite by which several priests say Mass together, all consecrating the same bread and wine. Occasions of concelebration are the ordination of priests and the consecration of bishops.

5. White (or Gold); Red; Green; Purple (or Violet); Black.

6. The erection like a bier in Masses of the dead, when the corpse itself is not present.

7. (a) Ordinary, (b) Ordinary, (c) Proper, (d) Proper, (e) Ordinary, (f) Ordinary, (g) Ordinary, (h) Ordinary.

8. Gregorian Masses are those said on thirty consecutive days for the departed.

9. (a) The foot of the altar, (b) the Epistle side, (c) the center of the altar, (d) the center of the altar, (e) the Gospel side.

10. The priest says these words at Mass before receiving the Precious Blood.

11. They are worn in Spain, and in the houses of certain religious orders, on the Feast of the Immaculate Conception.

12. These phrases form the opening of three different prayers recited by the priest during Mass.

13. Yes; at a pontifical Mass they are worn up to the washing of the hands before the sacrifice.

14. (a) Two, (b) four, (c) six, (d) seven, (e) twelve.

15. No, a priest is obligated to say Mass only on those days when the faithful are bound to hear Mass. The daily celebration of the Mass is a priest's privilege, not his obligation.

16. Kyrie, Christe, Eleison.

17. The celebrant of the Mass of the Presanctified on Good Friday communicates under the form of bread only, using the Host consecrated on Holy Thursday.

18. In various ways, it is made fifty-one times.

19. The following order: Kyrie, Epistle, Credo, Lavabo, Preface.

20. It is the Mass usually celebrated at the opening of courts, assemblies, and schools. The Mass is named from the red vestments worn by the celebrant.

GROUP SEVEN ANSWERS

PUBLICATIONS

1. The Paulist Fathers.

2. The Passionists.

3. It is a weekly journal, devoted to current events, published in New York by Catholic laymen.

4. Philosophic.

5. The Jesuits.

6. The Society for the Propagation of the Faith.

7. "Books on Trial."

8. The Franciscans.

9. "Spirit."

10. "The Newman News."

11. It is a national Catholic weekly newspaper, published at Fort Wayne, Ind.

12. It is a Catholic publication for physicians published by the Catholic Physicians' Guild.

13. "The Catholic Worker."

14. An evening newspaper printed and published daily in the City of the Vatican, issued under the oversight of the Papal Secretariat of State; a semi-official organ of the Vatican.

15. The Benedictines.

16. The Dominicans.

17. They are diocesan weekly newspapers published in Boston and Brooklyn respectively.

18. The Maryknoll Missions.

19. The Knights of Columbus.

20. It is a Catholic weekly, begun in Denver, Colorado, and now distributed through many dioceses of the United States.

GROUP EIGHT ANSWERS

THE BLESSED VIRGIN

1. May, the month devoted to the Blessed Mother.

2. It was the announcement by the Angel Gabriel to the Blessed Virgin, that she was to become the mother of God.

3. St. Joachim, of the royal family of David.

4. The fourth station.

5. It is the prayer spoken by the Blessed Virgin Mary in the home of St. Elizabeth after the Annunciation.

The canticle begins—"My soul doth magnify the Lord: And my spirit hath rejoiced in God my Saviour."

6. The feast of the Immaculate Conception of the Blessed Virgin Mary.

7. Fourteen years is often said to be her age; the real age is not known.

8. Under the Jewish law, a woman after childbirth presented herself in the Temple as did Mary after the birth of Christ.

9. The changing of water to wine at the marriage feast in Cana of Galilee.

10. The Immaculate Conception pertains to Mary's freedom from original sin from the first instant of her conception in the womb of her mother. The Virgin Birth pertains to the fact that Mary was a Virgin before, during, and after the birth of Christ.

11. To St. John the Apostle.

12. The journey to Jerusalem, when our Lord reached his twelfth year.

13. The Assumption is part of the tradition of the Church which holds that the Mother of God departed from this life and was taken body and soul into heaven.

14. (1) The prophecy of Simeon, (2) the flight into Egypt, (3) the loss of the boy Jesus in Jerusalem, (4) the meeting on the way to Calvary, (5) the standing at the foot of the Cross, (6) the descent from the Cross, (7) the burial.

15. These words were said by holy Simeon on the occasion of the purification of the Blessed Virgin in the temple (Sunday in the octave of Christmas).

16. St. Anne.

17. The angel Gabriel, who said, "Hail, full of grace, the Lord is with thee: blessed art thou among women."

18. The Immaculate Conception.

19. September 8.

20. About sixty-three years old is a frequently expressed opinion.

GROUP NINE ANSWERS

SACRAMENTS AND SACRAMENTALS (1)

1. It is an outward sign instituted by Christ to give grace.

2. They are rites, actions, prayers, and objects insti-

tuted and blessed by the Church through which we obtain special grace or favor of God.

3. Baptism, Confirmation, Holy Eucharist, Penance, Extreme Unction, Holy Orders, Matrimony.

4. No, but he must have the intention of conferring the sacrament.

5. The chief sacramental is the Sign of the Cross, which shows our membership in the Church of Christ, and professes our belief in the chief mysteries of our religion, the Trinity and the Redemption.

6. Baptism is the sacrament which cleanses us from original sin, and makes us Christians, children of God, and heirs of heaven. Baptism also remits actual sins, if the person baptized was guilty of any.

7. It is any portion of the body of a saint, or any object that has been closely connected with Our Lord or the saints.

8. It is that sacrament in which by the absolution of the priest and the acts of the penitent, sins committed after Baptism are forgiven.

9. Yes. If after marriage, say on the death of his wife, he became a priest.

10. The Holy Eucharist is the Sacrament which con-

tains the Body and Blood, Soul, and Divinity, of Our Lord Jesus Christ under the appearances of bread and wine.

11. A sacramental consisting of two small squares of woolen cloth attached to a cord so that one is worn on the back and one on the chest denoting that the wearer is spiritually associated with a religious order.

12. Matrimony is the sacrament which unites a Christian man and woman in lawful marriage and gives them grace to perform faithfully the special duties of the married state.

13. The creation of sacred ministers in the Church for divine worship and to rule the faithful. Minor and major orders precede the priesthood.

14. Two—Baptism and Matrimony (the priest is a witness, not the minister, in Matrimony, of which the man and woman are the ministers).

15. Baptism and Penance are called the sacraments of the dead because they take away sin which is the death of the soul.

16. The ecclesiastical announcement of the names of persons contemplating marriage.

17. Our Lord, at the Last Supper, when He said, "This

is My Body," and "This is My Blood," and "Do this for a commemoration of Me."

18. It is the sacrament which, through the anointing and prayer of the priest, gives health and strength to the soul and sometimes to the body, when we are in danger of death from sickness.

19. (a) Baptism, Confirmation, Holy Orders, (b) Matrimony, Extreme Unction, (c) Penance, Holy Eucharist.

20. A bishop ordinarily administers Confirmation but in extraordinary cases a priest delegated by the Pope may administer this sacrament.

GROUP TEN ANSWERS

SACRAMENTS AND SACRAMENTALS (2)

1. Holy Water is a mixture of water and salt blessed by the priest with solemn prayer, to beg God's blessing on those who use it and protection from the powers of darkness.

2. It is the custom among Catholic mothers of coming to church as soon as possible after childbirth, to thank God for His goodness and to ask His blessing on themselves and their children. A blessing is read by the priest on the occasion. ·

3. Baptism of desire is an ardent wish to receive Baptism and to do all that God has ordained for our salvation. If it is impossible to receive Baptism of water, Baptism of desire will impart sanctifying grace to the soul stained with original sin.

4. The obligation of secrecy on the part of the priest.

5. Baptism, because by this sacrament the soul is purified of all sin both original and actual, committed before Baptism, and without this purification we cannot enter Heaven.

6. The word, Viaticum, means provision for a journey, and it is now used exclusively to denote Holy Communion given to those in danger of death.

7. The name "mixed marriage" is given to a marriage between people not of the same faith—the Church is opposed to mixed marriages, since the husband and wife are divided on the important and far-reaching matter of religion.

8. It is absolution given simultaneously to a group without the ordinary confession, where such confession is impossible, as in the case of soldiers under fire. There is an obligation, however, of confession for the survivors.

9. No. Confessors, lawyers, and physicians are not bound to reveal impediments known to them through the discharge of their professional duties.

10. Excommunication.

11. This sacrament is conferred by bishops.

12. Confession is the telling of one's sins to a duly authorized priest for the purpose of obtaining forgiveness.

13. Yes, with special permission.

14. Confirmation.

15. In the United States, three times, during Mass, on three consecutive holydays or Sundays. For grave reason, a dispensation may be obtained to waive publication of banns. (Less urgent reasons may cause dispensation of one or two of the banns.)

16. Yes.

17. A mixture of olive oil and balm, blessed by the bishop and used at Baptism, Confirmation and other ceremonies.

18. "Teach ye all nations: baptizing them in the name of the Father, and of the Son, and of the Holy Ghost."

19. The ashes remind the faithful that they are themselves but dust and ashes, and that they should enter the season of Lent with a humble and mortified spirit.

20. A table covered with a white cloth, two candles, a crucifix, a glass of water and a spoon, and some holy water.

GROUP ELEVEN ANSWERS

SACRAMENTS AND SACRAMENTALS (3)

1. Except for the celebrant of the Mass of the Presanctified, only those in danger of death are allowed to receive on this day.

2. Yes, it is permitted, but is not considered a courteous preparation.

3. Other names are: Communion, the Sacrament of the Altar, the Lord's Supper, Corpus Christi, the Blessed Sacrament, Viaticum (especially when given to those in danger of death).

4. The process by which the substance of the bread and wine is changed into the substance of the Body and Blood of Christ in the act of consecration at Mass.

5. No, it is null and void, unless a papal dispensation is obtained.

6. It is not required but it is considered eminently fitting and proper.

7. Our Lord instituted the Sacrament of Penance, when He said to His Apostles, "Whose sins ye shall forgive, they are forgiven them: whose sins ye shall retain, they are retained" (John 20,23).

8. The ecclesiastical ceremony preceding Holy Orders in which the hair of the candidate is clipped or shorn.

9. The Sacred Roman Rota.

10. Holy Water blessed with special ceremonies and distributed on Holy Saturday.

11. No, an impediment of "spiritual relationship" exists between a sponsor and the person baptized.

12. True—this practice is found among those who follow the Oriental rites.

13. It is customary not to wear gloves.

14. When the Host is exposed.

15. (a) Holy Saturday, (b) it symbolizes the radiance and glory of the Resurrection.

16. To Blessed Catherine Labouré, in 1830.

17. No, only those who are authorized by the bishop of the diocese may give absolution, except that, for one in danger of death, any priest may absolve.

18. A sin which cannot be absolved except by a bishop or the Pope.

19. "I absolve thee from thy sins in the name of the Father, and of the Son and of the Holy Ghost."

20. Conditional baptism is that form of the sacrament used for a convert when it is uncertain whether there has been an earlier valid baptism. The ritual used in this case is—"If thou are not already baptized, then I baptize thee, etc."

GROUP TWELVE ANSWERS

RELIGIOUS ORDERS

1. It is the code of living for monastic communities, instituted by St. Benedict.

2. They are called "regular clergy" signifying that they follow a special rule.

3. To the superior general of the Jesuit order; it originated from his black cassock in contrast to the Pope's white.

4. The Benedictines, of which twenty-four members have become Popes.

5. She (1774–1821) was a convert; and foundress and

first superior of the Sisters of Charity in the United States.

6. The Order of Preachers.

7. (a) Poverty, (b) chastity, (c) obedience.

8. A "sister" is a woman religious who has taken simple vows, while a "nun" has usually taken solemn vows. The two names are often used as synonyms.

9. To orders of religious who go unshod or wear sandals as a form of austerity.

10. St. Ignatius Loyola (1491–1556).

11. The Paulist Fathers.

12. In general they are lay members of religious orders; i.e., men and women who do not live in community necessarily and yet may claim to wear the habit of the order and participate in the good works and devout exercises of some order.

13. Bishop James Anthony Walsh of Boston, superior general of the society, and the Rev. Thomas Frederick Price.

14. Fr. Isaac Thomas Hecker (1819–1888), convert, noted lecturer and champion of a Catholic press in America.

15. He is elected for life.

16. The "Passionists" (Congregation of the Discalced Clerks of the Most Holy Cross and Passion of Our Lord Jesus Christ).

17. The education of boys.

18. The Benedictines.

19. Rigorous silence, in which no monk is allowed to speak to another, except to the Superior.

20. (a) Congregation of the Passion (Passionists), (b) Congregation of the Most Holy Redeemer (Redemptorists), (c) Order of Friars Minor (Franciscans), (d) Oblates of Mary Immaculate.

GROUP THIRTEEN ANSWERS

HISTORY (1)

1. De Soto, in 1542.

2. Commodore John Barry (1745–1803).

3. Alfred the Great (849–899?), greatest of the Anglo-Saxon kings, who numbers among his translations from the Latin, Boethius' "Consolations of Philosophy."

4. He was a Roman Catholic, a member of the Continental Congress and a signer of the Declaration of Independence. He was also a member of the senates of Maryland and of the United States.

5. The pagan, Nero (A.D. 37–68).

6. A movement to revive art and learning of classical antiquity originated by Catholic scholars of the late medieval times and marking the transitional period from the middle to the modern age.

7. William the Conqueror, duke of Normandy, in 1066.

8. Désiré Joseph Cardinal Mercier (1851–1926), famous for his intrepid stand against the German invaders.

9. A great traveler, whose journey to China is told in "The Book of Marco Polo."

10. Richard Cœur de Lion, King of England. He took the throne in 1189 and died in 1199, at the age of forty-two.

11. An explorer, who discovered the sea route to India by way of the Cape of Good Hope.

12. Wars undertaken to deliver the Holy Places in Palestine from the hand of the Moslems. They began in 1095 and ended in 1271.

13. Constantine the Great (272–337).

14. First emperor of the Holy Roman Empire. Noted for military exploits, his codification of Frankish law, the reform of education and the development of agriculture.

15. For Lord Baltimore, who in 1634 founded the Colony of Maryland as an asylum for English Catholics, who were then under persecution. It is noteworthy that the Catholic colonists of Maryland permitted religious freedom to all Christians.

16. The *Nina*, the *Pinta*, and the *Santa Maria*.

17. Amerigo Vespucci (1451–1517), acclaimed discoverer of the mainland of America.

18. He was the victor of the second battle of the Marne and of the series of battles which ended the first World War. He was Marshal of France.

19. Balboa, in 1513.

20. Thaddeus Kosciusko (1746–1817) and Count Casimir Pulaski (1748–1779).

HISTORY (2)

1. The guilds; voluntary associations of religious, social, and commercial enterprises, and their members.

2. He became King of the Franks of Tournai in 481. His conversion followed his prayer for victory at battle of Tolbiac.

3. It is the place at which Emperor Henry IV, of the Holy Roman Empire, arrived to beg the pardon of Pope St. Gregory in 1077.

4. A group formally organized in 1852 in New York "to resist the policy of the Church of Rome, and to place in all the offices of honor, trust, or profit none but native American Protestant citizens."

5. Spain (1519–1556).

6. As a naval battle resulting in the victory of the Christians over the Turks and marking the beginning of Turkish decline in 1571.

7. Caesar Augustus, first Emperor of Rome (Luke 2,1).

8. Louis XIV of France (1638–1715).

9. In the Catholic Colony of Baltimore under Lord Baltimore.

10. Because of his red beard.

11. Richard I of England who reigned from 1189 to 1199.

12. He was prime minister to King Henry VIII.

13. John Cabot is the Anglicized name of the Italian navigator who sailed to the American mainland under the English flag in 1497.

14. Portugal. He was a discoverer and explorer and he greatly promoted the science of navigation.

15. This battle was fought in A.D. 312 between Constantine and his enemy Maxentius, and Constantine's victory was followed by his edict of toleration for Christianity.

16. It was the sentence passed on Christians destined to be mangled by beasts in the amphitheatres of Rome. In English it means "To the Beasts."

17. Ferdinand Magellan (1480–1521), the Portuguese navigator.

18. Ponce de Leon (1460–1521), Spanish explorer.

19. (a) Hernando Cortez (1496–1542), (b) Francisco Pizarro (1251–1324).

20. This picturesque title was given to the Popes from 1870 to 1929 during which time the Popes did not leave the precincts of the Vatican.

GROUP FIFTEEN ANSWERS

HISTORY (3)

1. He was the first bishop of Boston and was noted for his piety and devotion.

2. 1096–1099.

3. The medieval union of Church and State, founded on Christmas Day in the year 800, when Pope Leo III crowned Charlemagne emperor at Rome.

4. A movement originating in the University of Oxford about 1833 to restore to the Church of England certain Catholic practices without uniting it with Rome. Many of its members, including John Henry Cardinal Newman, entered the Catholic Church.

5. The Roman Catholic Relief Act passed under George IV, King of England, which once more admitted English Catholics as members of the State and granted other political rights.

6. It was the great council called in 1521 by Charles V, Emperor of the Holy Roman Empire, to try Martin Luther for heresy.

7. Franciscan priest, noted explorer of America, particularly the Mississippi Valley in the seventeenth century; he discovered Niagara Falls.

8. Constantine, in A.D. 330.

9. A false pope, who, though not duly elected, has claimed the papacy and attempted to rule the Church. There have been thirty-seven antipopes.

10. It condemned the Arian heresy; defined that the Son was consubstantial with the Father; formulated the Nicene Creed.

11. John Cardinal McCloskey (1810–1885) of New York. In 1875 he was made a cardinal. He dedicated St. Patrick's Cathedral in New York.

12. The Franks.

13. Natural son of Charles V who commanded the allied fleets that defeated the Turks at the battle of Lepanto.

14. Daniel O'Connell (1775–1847).

15. A suspension of fighting from Lent to Advent, from Thursday to Monday of each week, advo-

cated by the Church in the eleventh and twelfth centuries.

16. In this battle, Charles Martel (Charles the Hammer), leader of the Franks, defeated the Mohammedans, who never after attempted to conquer western Europe, although holding their power in Spain.

17. He was a Frenchman whose name has become a synonym for heroic courage and chivalry.

18. Stephen Langton, English cardinal, who with the aid of the barons forced King John to sign it. He was renowned for his scholarship and statesmanship.

19. Bartolomeo Dias (d. 1500), Portuguese navigator.

20. The premiership of France.

GROUP SIXTEEN ANSWERS

PRAYERS AND DEVOTIONS (1)

1. A general confession of sins in prayer form used in the Roman rite at the beginning of Mass and on various other occasions in preparation for the reception of grace.

2. The Rosary is a form of prayer, both mental and vocal, in which the fifteen chief mysteries of our faith are commemorated in a short contemplation

followed by the recitation of an Our Father, ten Hail Marys, and a Glory be to the Father.

3. Benediction is a short exposition of the Blessed Sacrament, at the close of which the priest makes the sign of the Cross with the Blessed Sacrament over the people.

4. A Creed is a brief statement of the principal truths which God has revealed and the Church teaches.

5. The custom of receiving Holy Communion on the first Fridays of nine consecutive months.

6. A three days' prayer or celebration.

7. An offering to God of religious practices and devotions for someone living or dead.

8. The hymn beginning "Stabat Mater dolorosa," usually sung during the Stations of the Cross.

9. The series of aspirations said commonly at the end of Mass or Benediction—"Blessed be God," etc.

10. It is the most frequently used Creed in the Catholic Church, and is so named because it states the doctrine of the apostles, and is thought to have been composed, substantially at least, by the apostles themselves.

11. The Prayer and Bloody Sweat of our Blessed

Saviour in the Garden, the Scourging of Jesus at the Pillar, the Crowning of Jesus with Thorns, Jesus Carries His Cross, the Crucifixion.

12. The Our Father, or Pater Noster, is called the Lord's Prayer because it was taught by Christ to His disciples.

13. A Novena is a nine days' prayer, said in preparation for some particular feast, or in order to obtain some special favor.

14. A pious exercise of prayer in union with the prayer of Our Lord in Gethsemane ("Could you not watch one hour with me?"—Matt. 26,40).

15. The Hail Mary, of which the first words were spoken to the Blessed Virgin by the Angel of the Annunciation.

16. On Good Friday, when the cross is placed on a cushion before the altar and solemnly venerated by the priests and the faithful.

17. A hymn, written by St. Thomas Aquinas, prescribed to be sung at Benediction.

18. Those prayers, beginning with three Hail Marys, are offered for the return of Russia to the Church, by decree of Pope Pius XI.

19. Any prayer said in a breath, having not more than twelve or fifteen words.

20. This devotion consists of pausing, meditating, and praying before each of the fourteen stations which correspond to the various incidents of the journey to Calvary.

GROUP SEVENTEEN ANSWERS

PRAYERS AND DEVOTIONS (2)

1. On Holy Thursday.

2. It is a medal modeled after an apparition of the Blessed Mother to Blessed Catherine Labouré in 1830.

3. The official prayer by which the Church, through her clergy, daily offers adoration and supplication to God. It is also called Canonical Hours.

4. (1) Jesus is condemned to death, (2) Jesus takes up His Cross, (3) Jesus falls for the first time, (4) Jesus meets His afflicted Mother, (5) Simon of Cyrene helps Jesus to carry His Cross, (6) Veronica wipes the face of Jesus, (7) Jesus falls the second time, (8) Jesus comforts the women of Jerusalem, (9) Jesus falls the third time, (10) Jesus is stripped of His garments, (11) Jesus is nailed to the Cross, (12) Jesus dies on the Cross, (13) Jesus is taken

down from the Cross, (14) Jesus is laid in Tomb.

5. The Joyful Mysteries—Monday and Thursday throughout the year, the Sundays from first Sunday of Advent until Lent. The Sorrowful Mysteries— Tuesday and Friday throughout the year, and the Sundays in Lent. The Glorious Mysteries— Wednesday and Saturday throughout the year, and Sundays from Easter until Advent.

6. Fifty-nine.

7. (a) To thank Him, (b) to petition His forgiveness and grace.

8. A liturgical prayer in which the clergy lead and the laity respond; usually marked by multiplication of praises of a given person such as the Blessed Mother.

9. The public chanting of a part of the Divine Office, taking place on Wednesday, Thursday, and Friday of Holy Week.

10. Vespers is the sixth of the canonical hours in the Divine Office, recited between four and six P.M. One portion of Vespers is the Magnificat ("My soul doth magnify the Lord"). "Vespers" literally means "evening."

11. This devotion consists of solemn exposition of the Blessed Sacrament on the altar for forty hours. It

commemorates the forty hours during which the body of Our Lord remained in the sepulchre.

12. It is a prayer to the Blessed Mother beginning with, "Remember, O Most Compassionate Virgin Mary, etc."

13. The Angelus is a devotion, performed in honor of the Blessed Virgin, at morning, noon and night when the church bell rings. It begins—"The angel of the Lord declared unto Mary."

14. One third of the rosary, or five decades, consisting of fifty-five beads on which are said fifty Hail Marys and five Our Fathers.

15. It is either one of two prayers, (a) The Lesser Doxology—"Glory be to the Father, etc." or (b) The Greater Doxology—"Glory to God in the highest," etc.

16. Each time, if made with a contrite heart, fifty days indulgence (Pope Pius IX, 1863).

17. The Dominicans.

18. It is a small piece of wax blessed by the Pope, symbolic of the Lamb of God, the Saviour; oval in shape, impressed with the figure of a lamb bearing a banner, with the coat-of-arms of the Pope on the reverse side.

19. A Latin hymn occasionally sung in Thanksgiving to God for some special blessings. "Holy God we praise thy name . . ." is one English translation.

20. The Nicene Creed, formulated by the Council of Nicaea of A.D. 325, is recited during the Mass on Sundays and certain feast days, after the reading of the Gospel.

GROUP EIGHTEEN ANSWERS

THE BIBLE

1. It comes from the Greek, meaning "Book."

2. This English translation was begun at Douay in France.

3. A word with different meanings. In general, it signifies writings, supposed to have remained long hidden, that claim sacred origin—but are not considered genuine. Often used by non-Catholics to signify what Catholics call deutero-canonical.

4. An alphabetical list of the words in the Bible, with an indication as to where each word occurs, and a short passage including the given word.

5. (a) On Sinai, Moses was given the Ten Commandments, (b) Ararat is the site of the landing of the

Ark after the Deluge, (c) Olivet was the scene of Christ's ascension into Heaven.

6. A member of the party of Pharisees of the Jews, a party which aimed to be "set apart from" all mankind by religious and political independence.

7. Greek and Aramaic.

8. It is the last book of the New Testament, chiefly prophetic, written by St. John the Apostle.

9. It is the branch of theology that investigates and expresses the true sense of the Scriptures.

10. (a) Judas Machabeus was a leader of the Jewish people, whose military feats are told in the books of the Machabees, (b) Jude Thaddeus was one of the twelve Apostles, (c) Judas Iscariot was the Apostle who betrayed Our Lord.

11. A high council of the Jewish people consisting of both civil and ecclesiastical judges.

12. The Vulgate is the Latin version of the Bible founded on the translation of St. Jerome and authorized by the Church.

13. A "tax-gatherer" employed by wealthy Romans.

14. A short fictitious narrative from which a moral or spiritual truth is drawn.

15. It is a Hebrew word meaning "certainly" or "truly" and is equivalent to the phrase "so be it."

16. Yes. But they are not bound to a literal interpretation of all the statements made in the books.

17. Yes. Even plenary indulgences can be gained by frequent reading of the Bible if certain other conditions are fulfilled.

18. They were Bibles chained to a wall or table during the Middle Ages to prevent theft.

19. The chief Greek translation of the Old Testament.

20. A sacred chant or prayer taken from other parts of Holy Scripture than the Psalms. Examples are the Canticle of the Blessed Virgin and the Benedictus.

GROUP NINETEEN ANSWERS

MUSIC

1. Ruggiero Leoncavallo (1858–1919).

2. He was the maker of Stradivarius violins.

3. The staff and Guido's Scale.

4. Gioachino Antonio Rossini (1792–1868), composer, great innovator and orchestrator.

5. Ludwig van Beethoven (1770–1827).

6. Karl Maria von Weber (1786–1826).

7. Wolfgang Mozart (1756–1791).

8. Gaetano Donizetti (1797–1848).

9. They are used to describe various types of chant in the Church.

10. Charles François Gounod (1818–1893).

11. George M. Cohan (1878–1942), actor, song writer, playwright.

12. Giovanni Pierluigi de Palestrina (1524–1594), noted for his reforms of liturgical music and his developments of polyphonic music.

13. Johann Strauss (1825–1899).

14. Joseph Haydn (1732–1809). His compositions include one hundred and twenty-five symphonies.

15. It is the Encyclical Letter of Pius X which regulates church music.

16. Giuseppe Verdi (1813–1901).

17. Franz Schubert (1797–1829).

18. It is the Roman form of early plain chant, and in 1903, Pope Pius X ordered its restoration as the sole chant of the Roman Church.

19. Franz Liszt (1811–1886), outstanding piano virtuoso and composer; he raised pianoforte to unparalleled heights.

20. "Silent Night."

GROUP TWENTY ANSWERS

THE SAINTS (1)

1. In the strict sense a saint is anyone officially approved by the Church for public veneration; in the wider sense, anyone in Heaven.

2. (a) Beatification is a pontifical declaration that a member of the Church deserves to be regarded as residing in Heaven due to a saintly life or heroic death, (b) canonization is a papal declaration that one already beatified is to be regarded as a saint and to be venerated everywhere.

3. Writings about saints, holy persons, and holiness.

4. A saint to whom special devotion is paid by certain people in certain places; one whose aid is sought in

137

special needs; one whose name is received at Baptism, Confirmation, or in religion.

5. Their death, which is their birthday to Heaven.

6. St. Joseph, the foster father of Our Lord.

7. He was an abbot, known as "The Father of Western Monks." He founded the Benedictine Order, and twelve monasteries.

8. A French girl who, in the year 1858, had visions of the Blessed Virgin, which led to the discovery of the miraculous spring at Lourdes. Bernadette was beatified in 1925 and canonized in 1933.

9. St. Boniface (675–754). He was the first Bishop of Germany.

10. St. Valentine.

11. The blessing of throats. He was a physician and a bishop of the Church. He was martyred about A.D. 320. His feast day is February 3.

12. St. Cecilia, "who sang in her heart to God only"; less often St. Dunstan is given this title.

13. St. Patrick.

14. St. Francis de Sales (1567–1622).

15. In A.D. 325, she made a pilgrimage to the Holy Land and discovered the cross on which Christ had died. This event is commemorated in the Mass of May 3.

16. St. Francis Assisi (1182–1226), from whom the members of the order take the name, Franciscans.

17. St. Joan of Arc, heroine of France, who was burned at the stake in 1431.

18. Stephen the Deacon, who was stoned to death.

19. St. Brendan of Ireland (484–577). Tradition teaches that he reached some part of the new world on one of his missionary voyages.

20. He was a French Jesuit missionary to the new world who was martyred by the Indians after years of work among them.

GROUP TWENTY-ONE ANSWERS

THE SAINTS (2)

1. St. George, whose name is most popularly known through the legendary account of his battle with a dragon.

2. St. Francis of Assisi is generally credited with having instituted the custom.

3. St. Apollonia.

4. A phial of his blood liquefies when placed near his head, although many centuries have passed since his death.

5. St. Christopher, who is one of the patron saints of travelers.

6. The Order of Preachers, commonly called the Dominicans, was founded by St. Dominic (1170–1221).

7. St. Theresa of Lisieux (1873–1897).

8. St. Thomas Aquinas (1225–1274).

9. St. Rose of Lima, Peru, who lived in the sixteenth century.

10. St. Peter Claver, S.J., Spanish scion of a noble family, devoted his life to alleviating the spiritual and bodily miseries of African slaves in South America.

11. She was the mother of St. Augustine, and was the means of his conversion to Christianity. She is the patroness of wives and mothers.

12. St. Joseph.

13. St. Thomas More (1478–1535).

14. St. Alphonsus de Ligouri (1696–1787). He was an eminent theological writer, noted for his devotion to the Blessed Mother.

15. St. John Vianney, the Curé d'Ars, nineteenth-century French parish priest, who was canonized 1924.

16. She was the co-foundress, with St. Francis Assisi, of the Poor Clares. She was born at Assisi in 1194 and died in 1253.

17. St. Thomas à Kempis was a German regular, generally associated with the authorship of "The Imitation of Christ." St. Thomas à Becket was an English bishop, killed by henchmen of the king in a quarrel over the rights of the Church.

18. St. Bridget (1303–1373), Sweden; St. Brigid (451–525), Ireland.

19. St. Vincent de Paul of France (1576–1660) founded the Sisters of Charity—he is patron of charitable works.

20. St. Francis Xavier (1506–1552).

ENGLISH LITERATURE

1. Religious dramas which developed among Christian nations in the Middle Ages.

2. Joyce Kilmer (1886–1918). His widow is Aline Kilmer.

3. G. K. Chesterton (1874–1940).

4. His books for boys, including "Tom Playfair," "Percy Wynne," and "His First and Last Appearance."

5. Thomas Moore (1779–1852), Irish poet and author.

6. "The Canterbury Tales."

7. Adelaide Anne Procter (1825–1864), a convert to Catholicism in 1851.

8. John Henry, Cardinal Newman (1801–1890).

9. Francis Thompson (1859–1901), English poet.

10. Alfred the Great (d. 901).

11. John Dryden, famous English poet and dramatist and a master of English prose.

12. The Arthurian legends.

13. Charles Warren Stoddard (1843–1909), a convert and writer of travel books.

14. He was an English priest who wrote one of the finest histories of England.

15. Francis Mahoney (1804–1866), who wrote under the pseudonym "Father Prout."

16. The Society of Jesus.

17. James, Cardinal Gibbons, who was Archbishop of Baltimore. The book is written to describe the Catholic Church, especially for non-Catholic readers.

18. Louise Imogen Guiney (1861–1920), daughter of General Patrick Guiney.

19. William Langland (1333–1399), one of England's greatest religious poets.

20. Coventry Patmore (1823–1896), English convert.

FEASTS AND FASTS

1. Festivals (or feasts) are certain days of the year which the Church wishes us to keep holy in a special manner.

2. On this day (the feast of the Annunciation) the Church celebrates the mission of the Archangel Gabriel, who announced to the Blessed Virgin that she was to be the Mother of God.

3. The octave of a feast is composed of the eight days which follow the feast.

4. Fixed or immovable feasts are those celebrated on the same date each year (like Christmas); movable feasts are those whose dates vary from year to year (like Easter).

5. The feast of the Resurrection of Christ from the dead; the "feast of feasts."

6. No, they differ somewhat from country to country.

7. The Friday in Holy Week—the day on which Christ died.

8. (1) Feast of the Circumcision, (2) feast of the Purification, (3) Pentecost.

9. The day before a feast, set aside for preparation, watching, prayer and generally fasting.

10. All Sundays of the year; New Year's Day, January 1; Ascension Day; feast of the Assumption, August 15; All Saints' Day, November 1; feast of the Immaculate Conception, December 8; Christmas, December 25.

11. Holy Week is the week before Easter Sunday, and it commemorates the Passion and Death of Our Lord.

12. The Circumcision of Our Lord.

13. Palm Sunday is the Sunday before Easter, and is the first day of Holy Week. It commemorates Our Lord's triumphal entry into Jerusalem, at which time the people threw palms under his feet.

14. All Saints' Day, a holyday of obligation, on which all the saints, even those who have not been canonized, are honored.

15. Pentecost (Whitsunday) is a solemn feast kept by the Church on the fiftieth day after Easter in honor of the coming of the Holy Ghost upon the apostles.

16. No.

17. Passion Sunday is the Sunday before Palm Sunday

and is so called because the celebration of Our
Lord's passion is drawing near.

18. The slaughter of the little children of Bethlehem at
the order of Herod, who sought to destroy the
infant Jesus.

19. Trinity Sunday is the 1st Sunday after Pentecost
and was instituted by the Church to honor the
mysteries of the Holy Trinity. It marks the end
of the Easter season.

20. January 6 or the feast of the Epiphany. In the early
centuries, under the Julian calendar, the birth of
Our Lord was celebrated on this day, by some
Christians.

GROUP TWENTY-FOUR ANSWERS

DOCTRINE

1. It is the theological science whose purpose is to
justify and to show the reasonableness of religious
doctrine.

2. Theology is the science of the knowledge which
we have or can have of God and divine things.

3. A truth contained in the word of God, written or
unwritten, and proposed by the Church for universal belief. Some of the dogmas of the Church

are—the infallibility of the Pope, the Trinity, the Divinity of Christ.

4. No;—as Cardinal Gibbons says, "Should a Catholic be so unfortunate as contumaciously to deny a single article of faith, or withdraw from the communion of his legitimate pastors, he ceases to be a member of the Church . . ."

5. A vow is a free and deliberate promise made to God to do something that is pleasing to Him.

6. (a) The faithful on earth, who are struggling for salvation, (b) the faithful in Purgatory, who are being purified of the last stains and consequences of their sins, (c) the faithful in heaven, who have attained salvation.

7. Not at all.

8. A summary of Christian doctrine, usually in the form of question and answer, for the instruction of Christian people.

9. It is One, Holy, Catholic, and Apostolic.

10. Tradition consists of the truths which have been revealed by God, but which are not contained in the Bible.

11. In these words Cardinal Gibbons speaks of Purgatory.

12. No; but Pope Benedict XIV (1675–1758) stated that it was a probable opinion which it is impious to deny.

13. The remission, in whole or part, of the temporal punishment still due to sin after sacramental absolution.

14. The Church recognizes the right of the State to use means which are necessary for the protection of the rights of its citizens, even to the taking of life. But capital punishment itself is not an article of faith, so Catholics are permitted to hold contrary opinions on the point.

15. Revelation: God's teaching to man of the truths that lead to salvation.

16. The age of reason is the time of life when one begins to distinguish clearly between right and wrong, to understand an obligation, and to take on moral responsibility—generally considered to be at seven years of age.

17. It means that God the Son became man, with a human body and soul.

18. Yes, it is necessary to be in a state of grace, and to have already obtained, by true repentance, forgiveness of those sins for which the temporal punishment is to be remitted by the indulgence.

19. The Beatific Vision is the direct vision or direct

knowledge of God, which the angelic spirits and the souls of the just enjoy in Heaven.

20. Contrition is a hearty sorrow for and detestation of our sins with the firm purpose of sinning no more, arising from love of God; attrition is imperfect contrition arising from fear of eternal punishment.

GROUP TWENTY-FIVE ANSWERS

SCIENCE

1. Marchese Marconi (1874–1937), Italian engineer. He installed the first radio at the Vatican.

2. Alessandro Volta (1745–1827), Italian physicist.

3. Wilhelm Konrad Roentgen (1845–1923), German physicist.

4. It was devised and established under Pope Gregory XIII in the late sixteenth century.

5. A Roman Catholic, known as the founder of the science of electrodynamics. The practical unit of the electrical current is named for him.

6. Johannes Gutenberg (1400–1467).

7. Louis Pasteur (1822–1895), famous bacteriologist and founder of the Pasteur Institute of Paris.

8. Galileo Galilei (1564–1642).

9. Louis Braille (1809–1852), who was blind himself.

10. He was an Italian physicist (1608–1647), who invented the barometer.

11. He discovered a method of producing synthetic rubber at low cost. He also contributed to the invention of Lewisite gas.

12. He was the founder of analytical geometry.

13. Luigi Galvani (1737–1798), noted Italian physician, famed for his studies of the electrical forces in muscular movement.

14. He is better known as Copernicus, developer of the heliocentric theory.

15. Gregor Mendel (1822–1884), author of Mendel's Law of Heredity.

16. He (1580–1637) invented a caliper which bears his name. It is a small movable scale which makes possible the reading of small subdivisions in measurements. He was a mathematician.

17. Albertus Magnus (1206–1280), Dominican friar,

scientist, theologian. Called "The Universal Doctor."

18. A monk, Roger Bacon (1214–1294), who was a member of the Franciscan Order.

19. Antoine Lavoisier (1743–1794). He described the true nature of oxidation and refuted the phlogiston theory.

20. Seismology, the study of earthquakes, in which it has led for years.

GROUP TWENTY-SIX ANSWERS

HERESIES AND "ISMS"

1. Heresy consists of renouncing one or more of the truths of the Catholic religion.

2. The belief in a worship of more than one God.

3. Free will.

4. One who, having been baptized, renounces the Christian religion.

5. The Jesuits.

6. A heresy of the eighth and ninth centuries, objecting to the use of images by Christians.

7. Arianism. Its leader attacked the doctrine of the Trinity.

8. A schism is a formal separation from the unity of the Church.

9. An infidel is one who has rejected Christianity as a divine revelation. A heathen is one who has never heard of Christianity.

10. Pantheism.

11. Providence and revelation.

12. A theory which claims, when applied to religion, that human reason cannot know God. The Church declares that, with the natural light of human reason, God may be known.

13. The exclusion of God and religion from life.

14. Predestination, which holds that God wills the salvation of some and the damnation of others by a direct act of His will.

15. St. Vincent Ferrer, O.P., and St. Dominic, O.P.

16. They rejected belief in original sin and the doctrine that grace is necessary for salvation.

17. Dualism, according to which the universe is the

work of two co-eternal and mutually opposed principles—good and evil.

18. The fallacious doctrine holding the ultimate salvation of all men.

19. The Quakers.

20. Lutheranism.

GROUP TWENTY-SEVEN ANSWERS

OLD TESTAMENT (1)

1. Those books of the Bible written before the coming of Christ, and, for the most part, accepted as canonical by the Hebrews.

2. "In the beginning God created heaven, and earth" (Gen. 1,1).

3. The first five books of the Old Testament, attributed to Moses.

4. Seven.

5. The Bible says merely "fruit."

6. Cain was the first-born of Adam and Eve.

7. The Messias (Matt. 22,42 ff.).

8. In the Old Testament, the flood that engulfed the world. The rain fell forty days and forty nights.

9. Noe: at the direction of the Lord.

10. Abraham was commanded to sacrifice his beloved son, Isaac.

11. Joseph, son of Jacob.

12. Moses was the great leader who brought the Jews out of bondage in Egypt. As a baby, Moses was rescued from the river by Pharaoh's daughter, and by her was given his name, meaning "saved out of the water."

13. A sling-shot and stones.

14. His tremendous physical strength.

15. A chest, containing principally the Tables of the Law, carried by the people of Israel in their wanderings and later deposited in the Temple at Jerusalem.

16. His patience under severe suffering.

17. Josue.

18. (a) "Great prophets"—Isaias, Jeremias, Ezekiel, Daniel, (b) "Minor prophets"—Baruch, Osee, Joel, Amos, Abdias, Jonas, Micheas, Nahum, Ha-

bacuc, Sophonias, Aggeus, Zacharias, Malachias.

19. Forty-six.

20. The Second Book of Machabees.

GROUP TWENTY-EIGHT ANSWERS

OLD TESTAMENT (2)

1. Genesis, Exodus, Leviticus, Numbers, and Deuteronomy.

2. It is a title for Almighty God (Daniel 7;9,13,22).

3. The city of Henoch.

4. They were the sons of Noe.

5. It is the tower that the descendants of Noe began to build which would reach to heaven.

6. Abram, meaning "a high father." Abraham means "the father of the multitude."

7. Lot's wife, for disregarding God's command and looking back on the destruction of Sodom.

8. Esau, oldest son of Isaac.

9. A ladder, which he saw in a dream, ascending to heaven.

10. Jacob, son of Isaac, to win Rachel.

11. A coat made by Jacob for his son Joseph, which made his brothers envious, so that they sold him into bondage in Egypt.

12. The water turning to blood; frogs; sciniphs; flies; murrain; boils on men and beasts; hail; locusts; darkness; death of the first-born.

13. The brother of Moses and a high priest of the Old Testament.

14. Forty years.

15. Saul, the father of Jonathan, David's friend.

16. His wisdom.

17. Elias.

18. The Books of Samuel.

19. The three Jewish young men who were cast into the fiery furnace by Nabuchodonosor, and were saved by an angel.

20. Jacob (Gen. 32;24-29).

FOREIGN LITERATURE

1. El Cid.

2. Hell, Purgatory, and Heaven.

3. Miguel de Cervantes Saavedra (1547–1616).

4. He (1639–1699) was a French dramatist and one of the world's greatest; his works display a keen psychological penetration and an exquisite literary sense.

5. His "Genius of Christianity."

6. François Villon (1431–1484), an able poet and writer whose romantic life still charms thousands.

7. It was the pen name of Jean Baptiste Poquelin (1622–1673), one of the greatest of French dramatists, noted mainly for his farces.

8. Ludovico Ariosto (1474–1533), author of many comedies and satires and one of the brightest lights of Italian literature.

9. An Italian novelist who is best known for his "Decameron." This and others of his writings greatly influenced the famous Geoffrey Chaucer.

10. Jean de La Fontaine (1621–1695), whose works rank among the most popular of French classics.

11. They were both members of the Carmelites and both are among the greatest mystical poets of Spain.

12. Torquato Tasso (1544–1595).

13. He was a French bishop of the late seventeenth century; a noted pulpit orator, a historian, and a controversialist.

14. Alain René Le Sage (1668–1747).

15. The drama; although both wrote widely in other fields and are among Spain's greatest litterateurs.

16. Henryk Sienkiewicz (1846–1916), famous Polish author.

17. French scientist and author whose "Pensées sur la Religion" are world-famous.

18. The sonnet.

19. He is famous for his history of the Popes.

20. Portugal. He has been called the most sublime figure in Portuguese literature. The epic is "Os Lusiadas."

PROPHECIES

1. Herod, who ruled at the birth of Christ, was an Idumean, a foreigner.

2. This prophecy was fulfilled when the Blessed Virgin Mary gave birth to Jesus.

3. Jesus was born in Bethlehem.

4. Our Lord was of the line of Jesse, father of David.

5. This prophecy was fulfilled by the slaughter of the children of Bethlehem at the order of Herod.

6. This prophecy was fulfilled by the flight into Egypt, whence Joseph, Mary and Jesus returned only after the death of Herod.

7. John the Baptist says of himself "I am the voice of one crying in the wilderness . . . as said the prophet Isaias."

8. Jesus spoke frequently in parables. "All these things Jesus spake in parables . . . that it might be fulfilled which was spoken by the prophet."

9. Christ gave sight to the blind and hearing to the deaf (Matt. 9,15–20; Mark 7,18; Luke 8,10).

10. Our Lord was sinless (1 John, 3;5, Epistles)—"and in him there is no sin."

11. This prophecy was fulfilled by the triumphal entry of Our Lord into Jerusalem riding upon an ass.

12. Judas Iscariot betrayed Our Lord for thirty pieces of silver.

13. Our Lord submitted to insults and violence without murmuring (Matt. 26,67—"Then did they spit in his face, and buffeted him; and others struck his face with the palms of their hands").

14. The soldiers, after they had crucified Jesus, cast lots among themselves for His garments.

15. "And Jesus said: Father, forgive them, for they know not what they do" (Luke 23,34).

16. When Our Lord thirsted on the cross, the soldiers gave him vinegar (Matt. 27,48).

17. The sufferings of Our Lord for the expiation of the sins of mankind.

18. "And the sun was darkened, and the veil of the temple was rent"—at the time of Christ's death on the cross (Luke 23,45).

19. After Our Lord died on the Cross, one of the soldiers pierced His side with a spear.

20. The death, descent into Hell, and resurrection of Our Lord.

GROUP THIRTY-ONE ANSWERS

THE APOSTLES

1. Simon Peter, Andrew, James the Greater, John, Philip, Bartholomew, Matthew, Thomas, James the Less, Jude Thaddeus, Simon the Cananean, called Zelotes, Judas Iscariot.

2. St. Peter was called Simon Bar Jona before his name was changed by Our Lord.

3. St. Paul, who was a Roman citizen.

4. The disciples of Our Lord were His personal adherents, numbering seventy or seventy-two. The apostles differ from the other disciples by the general power of jurisdiction and teaching. The apostles are Simon Peter, Andrew, James the Greater, etc.

5. St. John and St. Matthew.

6. St. Peter. His primacy is attested over and over again.

7. The gift of speaking so that all who hear can un-

derstand no matter what their native language (Acts 2;4–11).

8. Three: Simon Peter and Andrew, sons of Jona; James and John, sons of Zebedee; James and Jude Thaddeus, sons of Alpheus.

9. Because tradition says they were martyred on the same day in Rome. The day is the 29th of June.

10. He was a tax-collector.

11. The Holy Ghost came in the form of tongues of fire (Acts 2,3).

12. Thomas, he who doubted that Jesus had risen, unless he put his hands in His wounds—hence the popular concept of "doubting Thomas."

13. "And I say to thee: That thou art Peter; and upon this rock I will build my church, and the gates of hell shall not prevail against it" (Matt. 16,18).

14. The Gospel according to St. John, three Epistles, and the Apocalypse.

15. Saul (of Tarsus)—Acts 9. The use of the name Paul occurs in Acts 13,9.

16. St. John. Although plunged into a cauldron of boiling oil at Rome, he escaped unhurt and died a natural death at Ephesus about A.D. 100.

17. St. Paul, who wrote fourteen; St. James the Lesser, who wrote one; St. Peter, who wrote two; St. John the Apostle, who wrote three; St. Jude the Apostle, who wrote one.

18. Matthias (Acts 1,26).

19. He was a fisherman, and the son of a fisherman (Luke 5,1–11).

20. Andrew, brother of Peter.

GROUP THIRTY-TWO ANSWERS

ART

1. Madonnas.

2. Leonardo da Vinci—this painting is also called the Mona Lisa.

3. Raphael Santi (1483–1520).

4. Michelangelo (1475–1564).

5. Jean François Millet (1814–1875).

6. They were great Italian sculptors.

7. His landscapes.

8. Titian.

9. A great statue of Christ, erected at the boundary line between Chile and Argentina in the Andes Mountains. It is a symbol of the peace which they desire to exist between them.

10. An image of the dead body of Our Lord lying in the arms of His mother. Michelangelo's pietà was the only work he ever signed.

11. They were noted Flemish illuminators and painters.

12. Michelangelo.

13. The Immaculate Conception, which he treated twenty times.

14. Buonarroti (1475–1564).

15. He was a Dominican. His great frescoes are considered examples of purest religious art.

16. Diego Rodriguez de Silva y Velasquez (1599–1660). One of the greatest painters of all time.

17. Andrea del Sarto (1486–1531), a Florentine noted for his draughtsmanship and coloring. His Last Supper approaches Da Vinci's.

18. The Medici.

19. Florence, Italy.

20. A beautifully illuminated manuscript, choicest relic of Irish art, dating from A.D. 800. It contains the four Gospels, a fragment of Hebrew names and the Eusebian canons.

GROUP THIRTY-THREE ANSWERS

CHURCH GOVERNMENT (1)

1. It is a day with the obligation to hear Mass, and rest as far as possible from servile work.

2. A cardinal is an ecclesiastical prince, appointed by the Pope.

3. An annulment is a civil or ecclesiastical declaration that a supposed marriage was never valid owing to a known or hidden impediment. A divorce (in the common use of the word) is a civil separation from the bond of matrimony and has no standing in the eyes of the Church, since a valid marriage cannot be annulled.

4. A priest appointed by the bishop to care for the welfare of the men of the armed forces, religious communities, or institutions.

5. After his funeral, it is hung from the roof of the

choir of his cathedral, remaining there until it falls to dust.

6. A day on which persons between twenty-one and sixty years of age are restricted to one full meal, unless exempted by dispensation.

7. The whole collection of official services used in public worship in the Church.

8. "A spiritual censure by which one is excluded from the communion of the faithful. . . ." Major excommunication deprives a person of all church communication and is publicly pronounced; minor excommunication deprives him of participation in the sacraments.

9. No.

10. A supreme ecclesiastical ruler of a diocese: a successor of the apostles.

11. The voting papers are burned in a stove, and the resulting white smoke is the sign of successful balloting.

12. Lent is a holy season of forty days, preparing for the worthy celebration of the Resurrection—it is a time of penance, prayers and fasting; it commemorates Christ's fast in the desert.

13. The Easter Duty is the obligation to receive the Eucharist during the Eastertime.

166

14. The body of laws and regulations by which the Church and its members are governed.

15. The property owned and ruled by the Holy See, with extraterritorial possessions, mostly churches and palaces, amounting to about one hundred and sixty acres.

16. The fast of Lent ends at noon, on Holy Saturday, the Vigil of Easter.

17. Yes; if it is necessary for public health, as in the case of pestilence.

18. A day on which all those who have completed their seventh year of age are required to abstain from flesh meat.

19. No, he is not excommunicated. He is, however, gravely delinquent and should confess and receive Holy Communion as soon as possible.

20. (1) Advent and Christmas time, commemorating the expectation and birth of Christ, (2) Lent, with Holy Week, commemorating His passion and death, (3) Easter time and the weeks from Pentecost to Advent, commemorating His triumph and eternal reign.

CHURCH GOVERNMENT (2)

1. A section of a country and its population which is governed by a bishop.

2. He must be at least twenty-four years old.

3. Days of fasting and abstinence instituted for the purpose of doing penance and thus purifying the soul at the beginning of each quarter of the year. They fall on the Wednesday, Friday and Saturday following December 13, following the 1st Sunday in Lent, following Pentecost, and following September 14.

4. In the popular sense, it is the residence of a religious community of women, corresponding to the term "monastery" for a male religious community.

5. It is an agreement between the Holy See and a civil government on disputable spiritual matters.

6. A dispensation is the relaxation of a law in a particular case. It is granted when a law, made for the general good, may not be beneficial in a special instance.

7. No. It is forbidden by canon law.

8. Yes. Aquatic or semi-aquatic animals do not come within the law.

9. The Latin of official textbooks of the Church (the Bible and the Liturgy), as well as the Latin of the Christian writers of the West who expound and defend Christian beliefs.

10. Seventy.

11. It means to be made a cardinal of the Church.

12. A Eucharistic Congress is a gathering of the clergy and laity for the purpose of glorifying the Holy Eucharist by public adoration and general communions; and for the purpose of discussing means of increasing devotion to Our Lord in the Holy Eucharist throughout the world.

13. This is a popular term for the Promoter of the Faith, whose business it is to examine scrupulously all evidence of virtue and miracles attributed to the person who is being considered for beatification or canonization.

14. "Imprimatur" is a word placed at the beginning of a publication to show it has complied with the church law, and been examined by the censor. The word literally means "it may be printed."

15. It is that portion of a diocese under the authority of a priest legitimately appointed to secure for the faithful therein the helps of religion.

16. We abstain from meat on the day consecrated to

Our Saviour's sufferings as an act of worthwhile mortification, not because eating of flesh meat is in itself sinful.

17. Yes; it is required by church law.

18. It falls on the 1st Sunday after the full moon following the 21st of March (the Spring Equinox).

19. Apostolic delegate.

20. No, under canon law today, all cardinals must be priests.

GROUP THIRTY-FIVE ANSWERS

CHURCH GOVERNMENT (3)

1. He is, as it were, the counsel or attorney for the person whose canonization is being sought.

2. It is a periodic visit to Rome, obligatory for bishops. During it, the bishop visits the tombs of SS. Peter and Paul, has an audience with the Pope, and reports on his diocese.

3. In 1908, at which time it was removed from the jurisdiction of the Congregation of the Propagation of the Faith (not to be confused with the *Society* for the Propagation of the Faith).

4. An authority on ecclesiastical law.

5. The governor, a layman named by and responsible to the Pope.

6. A council of the priests of a diocese, called by the bishop.

7. It is the contribution given by a parish to the support of the bishop.

8. Usually fifty years, although there are exceptions, as in the case of Sister Thérèse of Lisieux.

9. No. The rank carries certain temporal privileges, such as the right to vote in papal elections.

10. A council to which the bishops, and certain others entitled to vote, are convoked from the whole world under the presidency of the Pope or his legates, and the decrees of which, having received papal confirmation, are binding on the members of the Church.

11. According to canon law, the minimum age is thirty years, as fixed by the decrees of the Council of Trent in the sixteenth century.

12. A letter given by a bishop to a priest so that the latter may obtain permission in another diocese to exercise his priestly functions.

13. That branch of administration which handles all written documents used in the official government of a diocese.

14. No.

15. Both are assistants to the bishop of a given diocese. The coadjutor is granted the right of succession; the auxiliary is without that right.

16. This term is used to signify the nomination to the cardinalate of a person whose name is not yet made public.

17. A penalty imposed upon a group of the faithful for serious violations of church laws.

18. It is from the Greek word meaning "the people" and is used to describe "the body of the faithful, outside of the ranks of the clergy."

19. It is a detailed account of the work undertaken by the Holy See for the relief of prisoners of war, refugees, and interned civilians.

20. An assembly of cardinals presided over by the Pope.

ARCHITECTURE

1. A building or portion of a church set apart for the administration of Baptism.

2. Romanesque.

3. The pointed arch.

4. A Latin cross.

5. Gothic.

6. A bell tower, more or less detached from the church building. This form of architecture is prevalent in Italy, and famous examples are to be found at Cremona, Florence, and Pisa.

7. An architectural support developed during the Gothic period of architecture for bracing the wall of a building, frequently like an arch.

8. Giotto di Bondone (1276–1337).

9. Its marble quarries.

10. A waterspout, usually found in Gothic cathedrals, often grotesquely carved.

11. The Cathedral at Chartres.

12. Renaissance.

13. Charles L'Enfant; his plans were carried out and the White House built by James Hoban.

14. Gothic.

15. Westminster Cathedral in London.

16. Byzantine.

17. Northern—France, England, Germany—although Italy has an excellent example or two.

18. James Hoban, a noted Catholic architect, won the competition.

19. Sixty thousand—its dimensions are seven hundred feet in length, four hundred and fifty feet in width in the transepts.

20. The adjective was applied in contempt by persons who regarded it as barbarian.

GROUP THIRTY-SEVEN ANSWERS

SYMBOLISM

1. The Cross.

2. It is a symbol of God the Holy Ghost.

3. Christ.

4. They signify the Holy Eucharist.

5. Aureole, synonymous with halo, is the name of the symbolic oval of light over the heads of saints in Christian art to symbolize their special honor in heaven.

6. Chastity.

7. Satan and sin.

8. It is symbolic of hope, because it was an aid to mariners against shipwreck. In modern art it is symbolic of St. Rose of Lima.

9. It represents the Church.

10. They are the first three Greek letters of the Greek name of Jesus.

11. The palm.

12. One that looks like an "X."

13. In honor of the Holy Trinity.

14. Jesus Christ, Son of God, Saviour, because of the Greek letters in the Greek word for fish.

15. Ave Maria.

16. It is the symbol, often seen, appearing like a P crossed with an X, standing for the first two letters, X (chi) and P (rho), in the Greek word for Christ.

17. From an ancient idea that a pelican fed her young with blood from her own breast.

18. They are the first and last letters of the old Greek alphabet and represent Christ who applied them to Himself, saying He was the beginning and the end.

19. The crook signifies that it is his duty to hook back the sheep wandering from the fold; it is pointed at the other end to signify his duty to goad those slothful in the faith.

20. St. Matthew—the head of a man; St. Luke—the sacrificial ox; St. Mark—the lion; and St. John—the eagle.

GROUP THIRTY-EIGHT ANSWERS

NEW TESTAMENT (1)

1. To the true cross of Christ.

2. The blessings pronounced by Christ in the sermon on the mount.

3. Between 2 B.C. and 7 B.C., probably in 4 B.C.

4. The Last Supper was the last meal taken by Our Lord with His apostles, on the night before His Passion. It was at the Last Supper that He instituted the Holy Eucharist.

5. Gaspar, Melchior, and Balthazar.

6. It was the trip, made by St. Joseph and the Blessed Mother with the Christ Child, to avoid His being among the victims of the Slaughter of the Innocents by King Herod.

7. He was a carpenter. He is the patron saint of carpenters.

8. Nazareth, his home, was in Galilee, a province of ancient Judea.

9. Procurator of Judea.

10. By St. John the Baptist (Matt. 3,13–17, Luke 3, 21–22, Mark 1,9–11).

11. Three years.

12. The fast of forty days and nights in the desert.

13. These words were spoken to the disciples of Our Lord on the occasion of the Ascension.

14. A voice was heard from heaven, saying, "This is my beloved Son, in whom I am well pleased."

15. Aramaic.

16. It means "anointed" or "consecrated" and is the Hebrew word for Christ.

17. Ten (Acts 1,3 and Acts 2,1).

18. Yes, one, when he saved from stoning the woman who was taken in adultery, "But Jesus bowing himself down, wrote with his finger on the ground." (John 8,6–8).

19. (a) The daughter of Jairus (Mark 5, Matt. 9), (b) the widow's son (Luke 7), (c) Lazarus, brother of Martha and Mary (John 11).

20. "The grace of Our Lord Jesus Christ be with you all" (The Apocalypse of St. John).

GROUP THIRTY-NINE ANSWERS

NEW TESTAMENT (2)

1. Two malefactors, known in tradition as Dismas and Gestas.

2. An angel appeared to St. Joseph before the birth of Our Lord and said, "Thou shalt call His name Jesus" (Matt. 1,21), and the Angel Gabriel said the same words to the Blessed Virgin (Luke 1,31).

3. It is a book of the New Testament written by St.

Luke the Evangelist, recounting the establishment of the Christian Church following the Resurrection of Christ and concerned chiefly with the acts of SS. Peter and Paul.

4. Zachary and Elizabeth.

5. The Gospels of Matthew, Mark, Luke and John; the Acts of the Apostles.

6. The Devil (John 8,44).

7. Matthew, Mark, Luke, and John, the authors of the Gospels.

8. St. Andrew, the elder brother of St. Peter (John 1).

9. They were both beheaded.

10. Of Mary, the sister of Martha.

11. Christ said, "He that is without sin among you let him first cast a stone at her" (John 8,7).

12. Ananias practiced a fraud in withholding a part of the price of land he sold for the benefit of the apostles; he was accused by Peter of lying to the Holy Ghost—"Thou hast not lied to men, but to God" (Acts of the Apostles 5).

13. The upper room in Jerusalem where Our Saviour celebrated the Paschal Supper, and instituted the

Blessed Sacrament. It was in the same place that the Holy Ghost descended upon the apostles.

14. At his own request, legend says. He did not deem himself worthy to die in the same manner as Christ, upright on a cross.

15. He spoke of St. John the Baptist, who was in prison and had sent messengers to ask Jesus if He were the expected Saviour (2nd Sunday of Advent).

16. It is found in John 11,35, in the chapter describing the raising of Lazarus from the dead.

17. St. Luke.

18. St. Paul uses these words in his first Epistle to the Corinthians; since then they have been used by other writers, notably Alexander Pope in "The Dying Christian to His Soul."

19. Lazarus of the parable was a beggar, who by his virtuous acceptance of poverty merited eternal reward (John 16,19–31). Lazarus of the miracle was the brother of Martha and Mary of Bethania and was raised from the dead by Jesus (John 16,41–44).

20. Between Ascension Thursday and Pentecost, the apostles gathered for nine days of prayer.

THE PASSION OF OUR LORD

1. The sufferings of Jesus Christ which had their culmination in His death on the Cross.

2. It was there that Christ underwent the agony in the garden, and was betrayed to the Roman officials by Judas.

3. The apostles, Peter, James and John.

4. It was in this manner that Judas betrayed Our Lord (Passion as read on Palm Sunday).

5. Thirty pieces of silver (The Passion according to St. Matthew as read on Palm Sunday).

6. It was used by Pontius Pilate when he led Jesus before the crowd; and is now used as a title for pictures of Jesus crowned with thorns.

7. They were Jewish high priests in Jerusalem at the time of Christ. It was they who led the move to have Him crucified.

8. Our Lord had said to Peter, "Before the cock crow thou wilt deny Me thrice." This prophecy was fulfilled and at the crowing of the cock, Peter remembered and "wept bitterly" (The Passion as read on Palm Sunday).

9. He hanged himself (Matthew 27,5: "He . . . went and hanged himself with an halter").

10. The hill near Jerusalem where Christ was crucified.

11. To the weeping women of Jerusalem, whom He met on His way to Calvary.

12. She was the noble Jerusalem matron who accompanied Christ to Calvary and somewhere during the journey offered Him a towel to wipe His face.

13. Simon of Cyrene.

14. The Blessed Virgin Mary; Mary of Cleophas, the mother of James and John; Mary Magdalen (Matt. 27,56; Mark 16,40; John 19,25).

15. "Jesus of Nazareth, King of the Jews"—written on the Cross on Calvary.

16. He was a prisoner at the time of Christ's accusation by the Jews. Pilate offered Christ's accusers the choice between Christ and Barabbas, which he should free, and they chose Barabbas (Passion as read on Palm Sunday).

17. A Roman centurion, impressed by the solemnity of the events of the Crucifixion.

18. (1) "Father, forgive them for they know not what they do."

(2) "Amen, Amen, I say to thee, this day thou shalt be with Me in Paradise."

(3) "Woman, behold thy son: son, behold thy mother."

(4) "My God, My God, why hast thou forsaken Me?"

(5) "I thirst."

(6) "It is consummated!"

(7) "Father, into Thy hands I commend My spirit."

19. The tomb of St. Joseph of Arimathea.

20. The salvation of mankind, gained by the death of Our Lord on the Cross.

SPECIAL GROUP ONE ANSWERS

1. The Ten Commandments.

2. Raphael, Michael, and Gabriel.

3. The mitre.

4. No, St. Francis had such reverence for the priesthood that he felt himself unworthy of ordination; therefore he remained a deacon to the end of his life.

5. Genesis, Exodus, Leviticus, Numbers, Deuteronomy, Josue, Judges, Ruth, Kings I, II, III, and IV,

Paralipomenon I and II, Esdras I and II, Tobias, Judith, Esther, Job, Machabees I and II.

6. He was king of Salem and the first man to offer bread and wine in sacrifice.

7. A Levite was one of the subordinate ministers appointed for service of the Temple. Leviticus is the third book of the Pentateuch.

8. A medal awarded by the University of Notre Dame to a Catholic layman of the United States in recognition of distinguished accomplishment for country or Church.

9. Chicago, in 1926.

10. Feed the hungry; give drink to the thirsty; clothe the naked; ransom the captive; harbor the harborless; visit the sick; bury the dead.

11. Notre Dame.

12. It is the liturgical book containing the Divine Office, the daily recitation of which is binding upon all persons in major orders and upon certain religious.

13. He has the rank of royal prince, given cardinals by the Congress of Vienna.

14. She was an Indian virgin of the Mohawk tribe;

known as the Lily of the Mohawks. Her beatification is now being moved.

15. Prudence, justice, fortitude, temperance.

16. He is a Chinese bishop, vicar apostolic of Nanking.

17. He was a poet, novelist and editor. Sent to Australia for his part in the Fenian movement, he escaped to America where he established himself as an author.

18. In the Gospel of the 3rd Sunday after Pentecost (Luke 15,1–10), in which Our Lord rebukes the Pharisees who have murmured against Him for "receiving sinners." He relates the parable of the shepherd and the lost sheep.

19. The Holy Ghost—from the Greek "consoler" or "advocate."

20. Henoch—"And he walked with God, and was seen no more: Because God took him" (Gen. 5,24).

21. The Eustachian tube, which runs between the ear and the pharynx.

22. Nero (A.D. 67).

23. The stiff square cap, having a number of ridges on top, worn by a priest, and signifying the crown of thorns of Our Lord.

24. A person who is undergoing instruction before Baptism and reception into the Church.

25. They are all Italian painters.

26. He was the defending general in the battle of the Plains of Abraham, which resulted in the capture of Quebec by the British.

27. Spain.

28. He was president of the Philippine Islands at the outbreak of World War II and managed to escape from the islands.

29. (1) Serious matter, (2) full knowledge, (3) deliberate consent.

30. Medicine, especially pathology. His name is given to certain structures of the human body.

31. His monumental "Lives of the Saints."

32. Eugenio, Cardinal Pacelli.

33. The monstrance or ostensorium.

34. (1) To hear Mass on Sundays and holydays of obligation.
    (2) To fast and abstain on the days appointed.
    (3) To confess at least once a year.

(4) To receive the Holy Eucharist during the Easter time.

(5) To contribute to the support of our pastors.

(6) Not to marry persons who are not Catholics, or who are related within the fourth degree of kindred, nor privately without witnesses, nor to solemnize marriage at forbidden times.

35. The small vessel of gold or silver in which the Holy Eucharist is carried to the sick.

36. The poor in spirit and they that suffer persecution for justice' sake (the eight beatitudes, Matt. 5).

37. The Resurrection, the Ascension, the Descent of the Holy Ghost, the Assumption, the Crowning of the Blessed Virgin.

38. "The Index of Prohibited Books" is a list of books, pamphlets, and leaflets which are specifically forbidden by the Holy See. The first Index was published in 1559 and there have been many subsequent editions.

39. Rubrics are the directions printed in red in the Mass book, prescribing the ceremonies and actions of the priest to accompany the prayer.

40. A hood worn by members of many religious orders.

41. Michelangelo.

42. Rev. Charles O'Donnell, C.S.C. (1884–1934), first president of the Catholic Poetry Society.

43. (a) The transepts are the lateral members of a cruciform church; (b) the nave is the central or main body of a church.

44. Yes.

45. On a religious publication, it means that the book has been examined by a duly appointed censor and that nothing has been found to hinder publication.

46. A staff, carried by bishops, abbots or abbesses.

47. The chalice used by Christ at the Last Supper, supposed to have been brought to England by Joseph of Arimathea.

48. Georgetown University, founded shortly after the closing of the American Revolution by the Catholic clergy in Maryland. It has been under the direction of the Jesuits since 1805.

49. The Sunday within the octave of Easter is called Low Sunday because of its inferiority compared with the great feast of the Resurrection.

50. The peacemakers.

51. They have all served in presidential cabinets, as (a) Secretary of the Navy and Attorney General,

(b) Postmaster General, (c) Postmaster General.

52. The second commandment—"Thou shalt not take the name of the Lord thy God in vain."

53. Jacques Cartier (1491–1557) discovered Canada in 1534. In the course of his explorations he ascended the St. Lawrence River to Montreal, and he named both the river and the city.

54. Father Damien was famous for his work among the lepers of Molokai.

55. These words form the 4th verse of the 22nd Psalm.

56. Long underground passageways which, in the early days of the Church, were used by Christians as places of burial and worship, as well as for peace and safety.

57. Gerald Griffin (1803–1840), noted author who ended his days a Christian Brother.

58. Gilbert Keith Chesterton, English author (1874–1940).

59. James Ryder Randell (1839–1908), a Georgetown College student.

60. Monsignor Robert Hugh Benson (1871–1914), an English convert, noted for his historical novels.

61. That space in the church reserved for the high altar and clergy.

62. The words occur in Matt. 16,19. In the preceding verse Our Lord had said, ". . . Thou art Peter; and on this rock I will build my church. . . ." He went on to say, "And I will give thee the keys of the kingdom of heaven . . ."

63. Any Catholic man who has completed his twenty-fourth year may be ordained a priest, provided he is not hindered by any impediment.

64. Requiescat in Pace. "May he (or she) rest in peace."

65. It means "good news" or "good tidings"—from the Anglo-Saxon.

66. Holy Thursday, a feast on which the Church commemorates Our Lord's Last Supper, when He instituted the Holy Eucharist.

67. (1) Your Holiness, (2) Your Eminence, (3) Your Excellency.

68. His apostles.

69. A room in a church where the vestments, church furnishings and the like are kept.

70. Its Passion Play, which was enacted before and was well-known by 1634.

71. No.

72. It defined in solemn decree the primacy and the infallibility of the Pope.

73. "The fear of the Lord is the beginning of wisdom" (Psalm 110,10; Prov. 1,7 and 9,10).

74. Doctor of Sacred Theology.

75. Notre Dame University.

76. (1) Humility, (2) chastity, (3) brotherly love, (4) temperance.

77. He discovered Brazil which he named Vera Cruz.

78. St. Anthony of Padua (A.D. 1195–1231).

79. "Confiteor" is the Latin for "I confess."

80. In February, 1929, when the Lateran Treaty recognized the temporal jurisdiction of the Pope over Vatican City.

81. It is called a cope.

82. John L. Sullivan (1858–1918), heavyweight boxing champion.

83. "The Anointed," from the Greek "Christos."

84. Nine. Latin, Greek, Syriac, Coptic, Armenian, Arabic, Slavonic, Georgian, Rumanian.

85. On the Gospel side, unless otherwise prevented, as by the bishop's throne.

86. The administrator pours ordinary water on the forehead of the person to be baptized, saying, "I baptize thee in the name of the Father, and of the Son, and of the Holy Ghost."

87. It means Christ mass and is a combined form of the two words. The word, "mass," in this case means feast.

88. "O Lord, make haste to help me."

89. It means "the coming" referring to the approaching birthday of Christ—Christmas.

90. The clean of heart.

91. It is also called the Lake of Genesareth, or the Sea of Tiberias.

92. To the Pope, because he is the successor of Peter the fisherman. Christ said to Peter, "I will make you a fisher of men."

93. St. Matthew. He wrote in Aramaic.

94. He says the Latin equivalent of: "May the body

of Our Lord Jesus Christ preserve thy soul unto
life everlasting."

95. They are made by burning the palms used the preceding year.

96. White or gold; red; green; violet or rose; and
black.

97. It is the annual round of the holy seasons and festival days, ordained by the Church, beginning with
the first Sunday of Advent and closing with the last
Sunday after Pentecost.

98. A Benedictine scholar of great learning and ability,
whose most important book is "The Ecclesiastical
History of the English People." He has been called
"the father of our English learning."

99. He was organist at St. Patrick's Cathedral in New
York and the composer of numerous liturgical
pieces.

100. The Stigmata consist of the miraculous impress of
the five wounds of Our Saviour on the body of a
person. St. Francis of Assisi received the Stigmata
two years before his death.

1. In place of the usual prayers of the Angelus, during Easter time.

2. The grant by which Pepin, King of the Franks, gave the Pope temporal authority over the provinces about Rome. This authority continued from 754 to the annexation of the Papal States by Italy in 1878.

3. In this council the religious revolution and erroneous teachings of Protestantism were condemned, and abuses were reformed. It was the answer of the Church to Luther and to the defections which followed after his heretical teachings.

4. It is a special vestment for deacons in the Church. Originally it was worn by the Pope only. It closely resembles a chasuble and is commonly used during a solemn high Mass.

5. Cardinal Newman (1801–1890).

6. St. Paul, in his second Epistle to the Corinthians.

7. He is the man whose ear Peter cut off in the Garden of Gethsemane.

8. "The Confraternity of the Most Holy Name of God and Jesus."

9. California. He was a noted Franciscan missionary (1713–1784); a fervent preacher; founded the first mission in Upper California, as it was then called.

10. Poetry.

11. "And the firmament declareth the work of his hands."

12. (a) Pope Leo X. (b) Pope Clement VII.

13. (a) Joris Karl Huysmans, French author, (b) John Moody, noted New York statistical expert, (c) Arnold Lunn, noted English author and sportsman, (d) John Henry Cardinal Newman, (e) Herbert Ellsworth Cory, dean of Washington University.

14. Prussian laws of May 1873, abolishing the Catholic department of public worship, persecuting the clergy, expelling the religious, and taking over control of legislation. The laws were moderated in 1886 and 1887, but not until 1915 were the Jesuits permitted to return.

15. Following the raising of Lazarus from the dead.

16. "There is no God" (Psalm 13,1; Psalm 52,1).

17. The Reformed Cistercians, popularly known as the Trappists.

18. The Dominicans. The title arose from a pun on their name—Domini Canes.

19. The Church has approved eighteen, any five of which may be worn together.

20. In this case, a person not present at the Baptism assumes the obligations of god-parent through an agent, or proxy.

21. He was a noted Polish soldier (1629–1696), famous for his battles against the Turks, who were threatening to overrun Europe. He defeated them at Chocim and Lemberg; his most famous victory over them was the raising of the siege of Vienna and their expulsion from Poland and Hungary.

22. St. Athanasius, a bishop of Alexandria, was awarded the title in the third century for his defense of the Divinity of Christ.

23. A sapphire.

24. It is from the Anglo-Saxon "lencten," and means "spring."

25. Admonish the sinner. Instruct the ignorant. Counsel the doubtful. Console the sorrowful. Bear wrongs patiently. Forgive all injuries. Pray for the living and dead.

26. St. Francis of Assisi (1181–1226). It is a beautiful,

brief poem on man's relation to God and nature.

27. He says—"Remember, Man, for dust thou art, and unto dust thou shalt return" (Gen. 3,19).

28. The celebration of Mass twice in the same day by the same priest, permitted when there are not enough priests to satisfy the needs of a community.

29. He is the national hero of Chile (1776–1842). Patriot and soldier, he led the Chileans in the revolutionary war against Spain and is hailed as the liberator of Chile.

30. William Caxton (1422–1491).

31. Fr. Bernard Hubbard, S.J. (1888–   ), author, explorer and scientist; noted particularly for his work in Alaska.

32. These words are said by the priest during Mass, at the washing of hands.

33. The educational system of the Jesuit order.

34. No.

35. Compline is the concluding hour of the Divine Office, recited immediately after Vespers. The literal meaning of "compline" is "finishing."

36. To a patriarch.

37. He was the son of an English Puritan divine, a convert to the faith and a poet, whose work is noted for imagery and metrical skill (1613–1649).

38. A prophecy, supposedly written by St. Malachy, Bishop of Armagh, and discovered in the Roman Archives in 1590. It contains Latin titles for all the Popes from Celestine II (1143–1144) to the end of the world. It is interesting, though declared fraudulent.

39. Feria is the liturgical name for all days of the week except Saturday and Sunday.

40. Fr. Abram J. Ryan (1839–1886), who served as chaplain with the Confederate army.

41. Fr. William J. Finn, C. S. P. (1881–   ), musician, composer, and author of "The Conductor Raises His Baton."

42. They were both English cardinals. Fabiola—Nicholas Patrick Wiseman (1802–1865), Callistus—John Henry Cardinal Newman (1801–1890).

43. (a) Visitation Nuns, (b) Ursulines, (c) Redemptorists, (d) Poor Clares.

44. Two books of the Old Testament are called Paralipomenon. They are also known as Chronicles.

45. One hundred and fifty days. It rained for forty days and forty nights.

46. El Greco (1548–1625).

47. A statue or picture of Our Lady that is black in color, because of age or of the material used. The most famous is in the Chartres Cathedral—the statue of Notre Dame de Pitié.

48. He was a noted English bishop (1691–1781). A convert, he studied at the English College at Douai; able theologian and controversialist.

49. "I sign thee with the sign of the cross, and I confirm thee with the chrism of salvation, in the name of the Father and of the Son and of the Holy Ghost."

50. They are ecclesiastical writers of eminent learning and a high degree of sanctity who have received this title because of the great advantage the whole Church has derived from their doctrine.

51. It means "fiftieth," and so signifies the elapsed time in days from Easter to Pentecost.

52. Wisdom, understanding counsel, fortitude, knowledge, piety, fear of the Lord.

53. Jacopo Robusti Tintoretto (1518–1594).

54. Dante Alighieri (1265–1321). It was the inscription over the gates of hell.

55. On Good Friday, in the Good Friday supplications.

56. It means "let him be accursed" and is used against those who are excluded from the communion of the Church.

57. It was fixed at this number by Pope Sixtus V in recollection of the fact that Moses chose seventy wise men to help him govern Israel.

58. Friars Minor, Capuchins, Trinitarians, Discalced Carmelites, Augustinian Friars, Minims, Passionists, Antonian monks, and the corresponding nuns.

59. A skull, from Latin and Greek words.

60. Eminent Flemish painter whose "Descent from the Cross" in the museum at Antwerp ranks among the greatest paintings of the world (1577–1640).

61. He was a saint and martyr of the Church; a duke of Bohemia, whose relics repose in the Church of St. Vitus in Prague, Czechoslovakia.

62. He was a Peruvian Negro and Dominican brother whose canonization is being sought.

63. The day before Ash Wednesday.

64. Modern pilgrimage made in England to Tyburn where numerous Catholics met death because of their religion during the reign of Queen Elizabeth.

65. Mexico—Our Lady of Guadalupe. Canada—St. Anne de Beaupré. France—Our Lady of Lourdes.

66. Days of solemn supplication to God for a good and bountiful harvest, for His protection in calamities, and to appease His anger at man's transgressions.

67. He was the first and only Catholic chaplain of the United States Senate; he was the author of several works of prose and poetry and a noted lecturer and preacher.

68. Two. Daniel Carroll, Maryland, brother of the first American bishop, and Thomas Fitz-Simon of Philadelphia.

69. Nine days.

70. His "Spiritual Exercises."

71. His poetry which is among the greatest in his century. He wrote in both Italian and Latin.

72. Two-thirds.

73. 1920 under Pope Benedict XV.

74. Order of Pius.

75. The bell rung for the Angelus.

76. Fifteen are prescribed.

77. The Order of Christ.

78. A residential bishop is one who resides in and is head of the diocese whose name he bears; a titular bishop bears the title of an episcopal see, but does not reside in it.

79. Without.

80. Roger Brooke Taney (1777–1864) and Edward Douglas White (1845–1921).

81. In 1854, by Pope Pius IX.

82. Yes.

83. The Council of Jerusalem.

84. It is a picture supposedly of miraculous origin.

85. "History of the Catholic Church in the United States" (4 vols., 1886–1892).

86. The Noble Guard and the Palatine Guard.

87. A day on which Mass may not be celebrated, such as Good Friday in the Latin Rite.

88. The Archbishop of Baltimore by right of the priority of the See.

89. Ad Majorem Dei Gloriam—"To the Greater Glory of God." It is the motto of the Society of Jesus.

90. This term refers to those Eastern Catholic churches formerly members of the schismatic Eastern Church, but later returned to communion with Rome.

91. Before beatification two certain and unquestionable miracles are required; before canonization, an additional two miracles after beatification are required.

92. (a) The Athanasian Creed forms a part of the Sunday office recited by priests, (b) the Creed of the Council of Trent is recited by converts on their reception into the Church.

93. St. Thomas Aquinas—these hymns are parts of "Verbum Supernum Prodiens" and "Pange, Lingua."

94. He was the only Englishman ever to become Pope, reigning as Adrian IV from 1154 to 1159.

95. The ceremony, in solemn Mass, in which the celebrant places his hands on the shoulders of the dea-

con, and says "Peace be with you." The Pax is then received by all the other attending clerics.

96. An ecclesiastical calendar containing the daily order for the Recitation of the divine office and the Celebration of Mass.

97. My Lord or Your Lordship.

98. St. James the Greater, who was beheaded by Herod Agrippa.

99. Samuel de Champlain (1570–1635), the discoverer of Lake Champlain.

100. Death, Judgment, Heaven, Hell.